The Illustrated Brighton Moment

The Illustrated
Brighton Moment

True stories
edited by Susanna Jones
and Lawrence Zeegen

UnMadeUp

Published by Unmadeup Arts, 2008
The Illustrated Brighton Moment

1 3 5 7 9 8 6 4 2
A CIP catalogue record for this book is available from the British Library
ISBN 978-0-9555860-1-9

Designed by StudioMakgill
www.studiomakgill.com

Typeset in Sabon and Monospace 821 BT
Printed in Great Britain by Antony Rowe Ltd

Unmadeup
Brighton
www.unmadeup.com

Supported by:

Contents:

Brighton and Hove:

🔵① Moment 🔺① Off map moment

Introduction:

The Brighton Moment

Brighton has always liked to catch the eye of a writer on the look-out for an atmospheric setting. Graham Greene's *Brighton Rock,* Patrick Hamilton's *The West Pier* and Helen Zahavi's *Dirty Weekend* all contribute to the town's reputation as a lubricious place to be. Brighton has also shown up in a variety of cameo roles in the writings of Jane Austen, William Makepeace Thackeray, Henry James, Jorge Luis Borges and many others.

To find out what the city means to today's authors we started with the simple idea of a 'Brighton moment'. It's that moment when you're going about your business or pleasure and something, or someone, pulls you up short. You hear yourself thinking, with a smile or a grimace, *Only in Brighton.* A Brighton moment catches the aberrant spirit that haunts this small city between the Downs and the sea. Perhaps the moment has been witnessed or endured. Perhaps it's one that *might* have happened, or is just about to.

The Brighton Moment began life in 2005 as a sparsely-attended cabaret-style event in the Festival Fringe. We (Alison MacLeod, William Shaw and Susanna Jones) asked writers to create and read short pieces expressing their own Brighton moments. Brighton is bursting with literary talent so this was easy. Prize-winning novelists duly took the stage alongside journalists, academics and biographers.

A bit like the city itself, 'the Brighton moment' has developed into something much more than its modest origins might have suggested. In 2008, the year of publication, it is now a major event in the official Festival programme. The Illustrated Brighton Moment brings together pieces created for those shows.

If we started with an idea of what a 'Brighton moment' might be, the writers who have responded to the call over the years have, quite magnificently, confounded us. Three years on, the Brighton

Moment – in subject, style and substance – continues to unfold as a colourful vision of a unique place. Our moments occur all over the town, from the Pavilion to Bill's Café to the Jubilee Library to a dominatrix's dungeon. They pop up on fishing trips, camping trips, nights in a club or days on the beach. There are moments from the distant past and moments from yesterday. There are lovers, chancers, criminals, a scary dentist, an evil seagull and – yes – a sexy seagull. Only in Brighton.

Susanna Jones

The Illustrated Brighton Moment

An Illustrated Brighton Moment, as chosen by the artists selected for this book, is one of any the wonderfully eclectic occasions that the city has thrown up – or been a backdrop to. The choice of moment, a short period in time, a specific instant, an important or significant occasion, was theirs to make – the only stipulation; it had to be a Brighton moment

Resist temptation. No flicking straight to the section of images, before reading a single word of text. We've all done it – picked up a brand new book (most often this works with biographies), noticed that the centre section, printed on rather attractive glossy paper, is a set of pictures and then fingered through it in seconds, happy to devour each image like cheap fast food fodder for the eyes. Of course, in truth, you've probably already done exactly this.

In this super-speedin', ever-changin', motivatin', cooltalkin', highwalkin', fastlivin' media age, we've become accustomed to taking on board thousands of images every hour of every day. We edit continuously; we have to, in order to navigate and negotiate the world we inhabit. Images have become instant hits of visual information – too often, we look but we don't see. This book is a very different affair – you'll need to look and see to get the most from the images within.

So, just how is this different from any other illustrated book? A good question, and one that can only be fully understood following a little insider info on the role of the illustrator. Generally, illustration can be described as a drawing or diagram that accompanies and complements a printed word – it is the art or process of producing or providing pictures to accompany a text, an example or comparison that helps to clarify or explain something. In a nutshell, illustrators create illustrations that give a visual meaning and presence to a writer's work. Chronology dictates that text precedes image; there is a natural order – a first and a second and a before and after but here, within the pages of *The Brighton Illustrated Moment*, the norm is cast aside and the illustrator and author are equal. Both have been given the same starting point and are free to describe their own Brighton moment. Each illustration depicts an individual illustrator's very own moment of choice.

Illustrated Brighton moments encompass the personal, the private and the political, the sexy, the sad and the silly. Some moments are location-specific – from the West Pier to West Street, from Snooper's Paradise to The Grand Hotel and from the Peace Statue to the Lanes. Unsurprisingly, the beach plays its part as does the rail link to the capital, yet beneath these familiar geographic locations lie themes of love and lust, drink and drugs, sex and sin, vice and violence – but, hey, it isn't all fun and games – there are also moments of beauty and banality, spectacle and surprise.

From the surreal sadness of Will Ainley's *Baked Beans on Concrete* – 'I witnessed a man sitting on the pavement scooping up baked beans he had poured onto the concrete, putting them into his mouth' – to Asako Masunouchi's longing to see an ice cream van that would never arrive – 'It came everyday with its melancholic sound, but I could never see it from my window' – each illustration is a visual expression of a moment, a time and a place, that Brighton has born witness to. Astrid Chesney found her own moment – *The World Beard and Moustache Championship* – and described it as, 'men from all over the world parading about like peacocks, displaying their incredible groomed beards and moustaches'. David Foldvari found his after accidentally running down a squirrel on the Upper Lewes Road – 'it still haunts me to this day' – while Jim Stoten recalls his uneasy moment thus: 'I would always go to the toilets in clubs when things were getting a little out of hand and I would look in the mirror and imagine things in the background behind my reflection…' Beans, beards, squirrels and mirrors – just a hint of the seemingly random, abstract and surreal elements that inhabit these illustrated moments.

So, take a touch longer than a casual flick-through – images may well be more instantaneous, more prolific and more disposable in the 21st Century; invest a little more time in looking and seeing these illustrations, you'll be rewarded with a rare glimpse into the moments that have moved, motivated and mattered to some of the most recognised practitioners of contemporary illustration. For each and every artwork visually describes the different tastes and flavours of these twenty-seven artists, all somehow connected and intertwined with a city in permanent flux – Brighton.

Lawrence Zeegen

Moment 1:
Novelty Acts for the Broken-Hearted
by David Bramwell

Go look for the Basement Club on Grand Parade now and you won't find it. Legend has it someone left the Ace of Spades playing on a loop one night and the whole place quietly imploded.

The truth is more prosaic.

The Basement was a dank, cavernous pit of cheap garden furniture, plastic pint glasses that leaked down your leg, sweaty walls, choking heat and a smell of old people's homes. At weekends it played host to hordes of pasty-faced indie kids, whose only regular exercise seemed to be throwing themselves around to the Pixies.

Weird Glen was a permanent fixture, dressed like some latter-day Jim Morrison. Legend had it Glen used to make his own acid, and in a police raid once gobbled up his entire month's stash and deep-fried his brain.

I once saw him spend an entire evening in there, licking off the sweat that shimmied constantly down the walls.

And it was there, one Wednesday evening, that I found the Zincbar: a fortnightly amateur cabaret. Brighton's answer to the Gong Show. Zincbar's host was Adrian Bunting. Square-headed and arrogant, Adrian would swagger on stage, fag and pint in hand, dispensing with gags in favour of just shouting until his voice was hoarse, imploring us to adore each act like they were God's chosen ones. When it came to peddling shoddy goods, Adrian was a terrific salesman.

The rules were simple: anyone – no matter how talentless, pissed or mentally unstable – had five minutes in which to entertain us any way they saw fit. Heckling was out. As Adrian said, If you don't like it, come and do something better yourself. And if the heckling continued, he'd resort to violence.

Though the acts varied every fortnight, the Zincbar did have its legendary regulars. First up was Marty, an intense, ageing ex-college professor from Brooklyn. At nine o'clock, Marty's dishevelled rambling figure would appear in the crowd, weaving its way through towards the stage. His narratives ranged from Battle of the Somme to occult sciences, but his habit of side-tracking himself with bizarre anecdotes meant the initial thread of the story was lost forever.

Dave Suit was our resident Situationist. Whatever that meant. The first time I saw him perform, he sat in a swivel chair on stage, drinking greedily from a whisky bottle and spinning round and round and round until eventually, inevitably, he fell off, landed in the lap of an attractive girl on the front row and promptly threw up.

The Tartan Warrior was the only act I've ever seen who managed to get worse with experience. He tried everything: stand-up comedy, juggling, body-popping, singing, magic tricks... Until finally his act devolved into him just sitting on the stage wanking. And crying. We adored him. It was like watching somebody else acting out your own worst nightmares.

It was empowering to know that whatever happened when you went on stage, it would never be as bad as that.

And I did get on stage.

To tell my stories for the first time.

One night, Adrian asked if I'd compère for the following month while he was away in Edinburgh. He offered me eighty quid. I couldn't say no.

Dave Suit turned up that night with a bucket full of plaster of Paris. His girlfriend put a muslin sheet over him and proceeded to paint. After ten minutes his entire body was covered in white goo. Within half an hour he'd set solid. There he remained for the rest of the evening.

For my finale as compère I decided to write a limerick on different parts of my body and remove my clothes to the Stripper music, revealing the limerick one line at a time.

> There once was a mouse called Keith
> Who circumcised boys with his teeth
> It wasn't for leisure
> Or sexual pleasure
> But to get to the cheese underneath!

But as my naked frame was finally revealed, Weird Glen came running on stage. He was also naked, having taken my undressing as a cue for a night of all-in naturism. He rugby-tackled me and for a moment it was like we were in some bizarre gay wrestling porn film. And as we cavorted around on the floor I rolled in something wet and sticky. Dave Suit, trapped inside the plaster of Paris for over three hours, had finally pissed himself.

The Basement was demolished in 1998. The Zincbar performers either died or moved away. Only Weird Glen remains, drifting round North Laine like a lonely ghost.

What other town would have offered me the opportunity, in front of two hundred people, to roll around naked in another man's urine?

For a short while the Zincbar was my home. A cabaret of misfits. Novelty acts for the broken-hearted. A freak show for our time. It's where my writing first began and my career as a stripper ended.

Thank you Brighton.

Moment 2:
The Wink
by Madeleine Cary

Gillian's house was truly Brightonian. It was an organic house which had changed and grown with nurture over the years. She had bought it a quarter of a century ago when it was an unloved squat. At the time, it had cost her only twenty-five thousand pounds. Now it was worth half a million. There was a mathematical equation in there about economic growth and inflation, but Gillian dwelt only on the corollaries of human life: lovers, births, growths, departures and returns.

The house was an end-of-terrace, making its side wall an irresistible canvas to graffiti artists. Gillian had only just finished having the whole exterior of the house re-painted. The graffiti was obliterated, cracks were filled, mouldy window frames were replaced and now her home had the perfect shell: a coat of soft lavender with crisp white satin on the woodwork. Gillian delighted in how cherished her house looked. It made her think of gingerbread, of dolls' houses. She had it all to herself now that the kids had grown and flown. It was her chateau, her sanctum sanctorum. She thought she might buy a shotgun and stand at the shuttered windows to keep the graffiti artists and other ne'er-do-wells at bay.

One day Gillian returned home to find an ugly scrap of paper had been taped to the side wall. It was lined paper from a notepad, scrawled on in bright green marker. DO YOU WANT DRUGS? the message said. IF SO, PHONE THIS NUMBER. A mobile number was scribbled across the bottom of the sheet. A brown sliver of a dog-end – from a rolled cigarette or a joint – was taped to the top edge of the paper. Gillian's heart raced. She looked around to see if she was being watched. Surely none of her friends would think she'd find this kind of vandalism amusing? Everyone who knew her was familiar with the story of the house and its associations with drugs.

Twenty-five years earlier, she'd been warned by the estate agent who took her to view the place that they were having trouble selling it because of its reputation as a squat and a dealer's den. Worse, the

squatters were quick to put all viewers off with tales of a ghost –
a trench soldier with half his face blown off – and rats the size of
raccoons which scratched and screeched in the walls. The price on
the place was plummeting by the day. In the end, it had all worked
in Gillian's favour and she'd got a house with three bedrooms for
the price of a one bedroom flat. But it was some time before friends
stopped making jokes about scoring and dealing every time they
came to visit.

The writing on the note looked decidedly childish. Gillian
looked around again. No one was watching. She pulled gently at
the sticky tape so it wouldn't remove any of the soft lavender paint.
She had the paper with the disgusting dog-end in her hand. She was
about to screw it into a ball but thought better of it. I'll phone the
damn number, she thought. I'm not being taken for a fool.

It was only when she heard the ringing on the other end of the
phone that she realised no one who was actually dealing in drugs
would dream of posting up their own number. Or would they? The
laws had relaxed. It was a different world out there.

'Hello?' a young male voice answered.

'Hello,' Gillian said. 'I thought you ought to know that I didn't
find your joke very funny.'

'What joke?' the voice asked.

Gillian explained about the crude note.

'*What?*' The boy's voice cracked. 'Do you really think if I was a
drug dealer I'd go and stick my number up in public?'

'No. You're right,' said Gillian. 'I'm sorry. It must be a silly
prank someone's played on you.'

'Yeah,' said the boy. 'How sad is that?'

'How old are you?' Gillian asked, unsure of what else to say.

'Seventeen,' he replied. 'Look, who are you, anyway?'

Gillian gave her name and asked the boy his. He was Jake. They
both stopped speaking for a moment. Gillian felt foolish for making
the call and upsetting this young man.

'Look, Jake,' she said, 'don't worry. I'll throw the note in the bin.
Think no more of it.'

She was signing off with more apologies when the boy slammed
the phone down. He hadn't needed to say it; he obviously thought
she was a sad, interfering old biddy. As she dropped the torn-up note
into the bin, she felt a dead weight inside her. She wished she could
erase the phone call. Or, better, she wished she could invite this Jake

round some time. She'd tell him how, when she was his age, she'd rolled in the mud at the first Isle of Wight Festival while on stage Jimi Hendrix played the guitar with his teeth. She'd tell him about the time she lived in a squat in Copenhagen with Vietnam draft dodgers. Or about all those years she'd spent raising her kids alone in this ramshackle old place, never having the time or the inclination to worry about how smart or clean it looked.

Some five minutes later, the phone rang. Gillian's first thought was that it was Jake. He'd probably got to the bottom of the prank and was letting her know who was responsible.

'Are you the woman who just accused my son of being a drug dealer?' It was a deep voice, growling with threat.

'Oh, not at all,' Gillian poured out. She went on to explain the whole situation.

'Well, he's still upset about it,' the man said. 'You can't be too concerned when it comes to drugs and young kids, can you?'

'Quite right,' Gillian said, 'and this area has had its problems in the past.'

The man asked her where she lived. She gave him the name of her street and told the colourful tale of how the place had been a local dealer's den before she'd bought it all those years ago. There was a long silence on the end of the line.

'Are you Gillian at Number 12?' the man asked, finally.

Gillian's heart danced a jig. 'Yes,' she said cautiously. 'It's me. Who are you? Do I know you?'

'I don't believe it,' the man said. 'I'm Ricky.'

'*Ricky?*'

A door opened on the past. Twenty-five years ago. The smell of the place was the worst: unwashed bodies and hair, rancid curry dishes, stale booze. And the smoke: cigarettes, incense, pipes and bongs. Every room a chaos of old mattresses and blankets, windows draped with sheets, surfaces covered in sticky candle wax, ashtrays, occasional needles. In one room an indistinct group of people sat in silhouette against candlelight, ignoring her completely. In another, a solitary man padded mournfully on a bongo. The estate agent looked like he wanted to be sick. The carpets buzzed with fleas which danced around her ankles. The walls on the stairway were decorated with silver threads from the snails and slugs that crawled up from the basement.

But Gillian had seen through the squalor. In her vision of the future, this would be where she and her two children could finally settle into a real house, where they'd all have rooms of their own. It was a single parent's dream. If only she could think of some way to get the squatters to leave.

It was at that precise moment that a young man had popped his head out from one of the rooms. His angular face was topped by a nest of gothic blue-black hair and a solitary earring – radical in its day – glittered in his ear.

'Hi,' he said, 'I'm Ricky. You looking to buy this place?'

'Well, yes,' Gillian said. 'I'm a single mum and it would be ideal.'

'Oh, yeah?' he said. 'My mum was on her own, too. Look, why don't you come in.'

She followed him into a big bay-windowed room. It was so much cleaner and brighter than the others. A waifish girl with a striking haircut was curled up on the bed, reading a book. On the main wall a huge lurid chalk drawing had been etched into the woodchip wallpaper. It was of a serene three-eyed face. The two eyes at the side were closed, but the middle eye, bright and hypnotic, was open. Ricky saw Gillian looking at it.

'If you come over here,' he said, leading her to the middle of the room, 'the middle eye is shut. Look.'

It was true. Some shiny material over the eye and a trick of the light made it look closed. If you moved to the side, it winked at you.

Everything had happened so quickly after that. Gillian had shared a tea with the couple and heard all about their woes. Ricky was the ringleader who'd started the squat in the first place, but now he'd tired of the incessant flow of people he didn't even know. But he and his girlfriend loved their own room and wanted to stay on. It was a simple arrangement in the end; Ricky had promised Gillian that he would find the others another squat and, in return, Gillian agreed that if she bought the house, Ricky and his girlfriend could stay there rent-free for as long as they wanted. She knew, of course, that co-habiting with a single mum and two kids would soon lose its appeal.

Everyone questioned her sanity. *Squatters? Under English law they can stay there forever!* But Gillian was soon proven right. Ricky got the others out, the sale went ahead and, just days after she and the children had moved in, just as they'd started to gut the place, he and his girlfriend decided to move on.

It was about a year later that the article appeared in the newspaper. Ricky had been done for dealing and sent down. Gillian could remember it all now. How upset she'd been at the time. How she'd wondered if things might have turned out differently if Ricky and his girlfriend had stayed in the house longer.

'I can't believe it's you,' she was saying now to this much older version of Ricky. Neither of them quite knew what to say next.

Finally, Ricky muttered, 'I'm sorry we had to catch up in such weird circumstances.'

'Well, that's Brighton for you,' Gillian said. She wanted to ask if he still had blue-black hair, or, even, if he still had hair. But all she could manage was to ask him how old he was now.

'Forty-two,' he said, his voice rising in disbelief. Then he laughed as though the idea of him being so old struck him as a joke.

Gillian joined in the laughter then said, 'Jake sounds like a real credit to you.'

'Oh, he is. Thank God he's not like his old dad. He's a good boy, he is. He's off to Uni next year.'

'Oh, that's wonderful,' Gillian said. 'And, Ricky, you know, you really were welcome to stay in the house all those years ago. You didn't need to move out.'

Ricky laughed again. 'Oh, I know that. But that girl I was with then didn't have a clue. She kept saying you'd turn into an interfering old biddy.'

Gillian giggled as the coincidence rippled through her. It was almost comic the way time stretched and bounced back and met itself in the middle.

'And you, Ricky?' she asked. 'What did you think?'

'You were cool,' he said. 'Really cool.'

Later, Gillian went into her lovely bay-fronted living room. *Cool.* The word made her smile. *Really cool.*

And though she'd scraped and papered and painted that wall over the years, she thought she could make out a ghostly impression. Yes, if she looked hard enough, it was there. The lurid three-eyed creature. Through the soft stone-coloured paint, that bright, wise middle eye was winking at her.

Moment 3:
Shock Waves
by Rose Collis

I Was Sure The Waves Would Kill Me.

It's not often that The Argus has a headline that catches my attention, certainly not the *Noisy Cockerel Rustles Neighbours' Feathers* variety. But then I was sitting in front of said waves, having a coffee, while the wind did its best to turn the low tide into a frenzy of froth and my paper into pulp. The quote came from one Andy Mills who, on Christmas Day 2007, decided it was a good idea to go for a swim off Brighton beach in a freezing sea of eight-foot waves.

I could have told him that a winter storm isn't always necessary to instil terror along this coastline. Even on a calm day, if you stare intently at the English Channel long enough (thirty seconds usually does it for me), it takes on another form entirely. When I do this, I face my recurring nightmare: a wall of water heading straight for me. Brighton and Hove esplanade is perfect for this type of self-torture because it's a nice, flat vista. But why do I subject myself to a daytime version of my nocturnal terror? They say that sometimes you have to face your worst fears in order to overcome them, but – in my opinion – anyone who falls for that line deserves to have nightmares.

Tidal waves are nothing new. Of course, everyone knows them as *tsunamis* nowadays, and we know what they look like and what they can do. But not when I was growing up in the 1960s and, somehow, my imagination conjured up a terrifying tidal wave that has visited me regularly since I was about six. The scenario is always the same.

It's a warm, sunny day and I'm on a packed, pebbly beach, along with many other people. People are enjoying themselves with the usual seaside activities: paddling, picnicking, making sandcastles or just lazing about on towels or in deckchairs.

So busy, in fact, that they don't see what I see.

Heading straight for us all is a huge wall of water: dark, roaring, and rearing up over our heads. I'm pointing at it and shouting a warning to everyone on the beach, except, of course, because it's a nightmare, there's no sound coming out of my mouth and I can't run fast enough. On more than one occasion, the wave comes right over my head, casting a dark shadow. This is usually the point at which I wake up, sweaty and shaking.

I'm in good company. Sir Alec Guinness, who completed his basic naval training at the HMS King Alfred site (formerly Hove Marina), once revealed, 'Tidal waves have always presented an ultimate nightmare in my imagination and I cannot trace the source of this phobia...'

Perhaps, then, it's some sort of genetic memory. For, like many of my ancestors, water is the dominant element – at least in my psyche. My forebears included at least two mariners, a Kentish bargeman and a London wharfinger (though that sounds more like a Bond villain than an occupation). One of the earliest pictures taken of me shows me in a park, peering into a harmless stream. Apparently, this wasn't dangerous enough to satisfy me and, shortly afterwards, I was peering into a deep pond on Wimbledon Common when I toppled in head-first. This was a challenging scenario for my accompanying uncle who, like me, couldn't swim. It was thirty years before I learned about this incident and was thus finally able to pinpoint the source of a fear that had baffled me and my poor mother for years: getting water in my face. Neither of us ever understood why, every bath-time, our home became a house of horrors, where I provided a diverse array of blood-curdling shrieks.

But now it appears that, like me and Alec, others are beginning to have watery nightmares. There's a rising tide of concern about waves that might hit the South Coast in the future and the havoc they would wreak on seaside communities and habitats. There are fears that if the volcano Cumbre Vieja on La Palma in the Canary Islands erupts, it will cause enough of its western flank – consisting of millions of tons of rock – to fall into the sea and spark a mega-tsunami. Waves of around ten to forty metres could hit resorts and ports along the South Coast within hours of the collapse. This danger has now been added to the long list of concerns about the proposed redevelopment of the King Alfred site – Alec's old haunt – and, specifically, the Gehry Tower. Yes, on top of all the objections that the development would be a blot on the landscape, and that the tower looks like two drag queens on a windy day, some Argus correspondents have pointed out the dangers of building high-density homes on low-lying, unprotected coastlines. Perhaps, like me, they've got their own genetic memories.

On the afternoon of Saturday 20th July 1929, hundreds of people are still enjoying the sultry weather of a glorious summer's day. It's been an unusually dry summer and Brighton Corporation Waterworks have been appealing to the public to conserve water, especially as the town is full of visitors come to partake of the seaside attractions; popular vaudevillian George Carney is appearing at the Grand Theatre, while Sam and Sue the sealions are entertaining families at the Aquarium. The destroyer HMS Centaur is moored between the Palace and West Piers for the weekend, and is welcoming sightseers on board.

The Brighton Herald *Notes of the Week* that day observes (somewhat presciently as it transpires), *There are many occasions where Brightonians seem sublimely indifferent to their greatest possession – the sea*. This day, that sea is calm but the air is sticky, almost thick enough to bite, and a summer storm this evening seems inevitable. The tide is an unusually long way out; east of the Palace Pier, around thirty-five feet of sand has been exposed, more sand than is normal on the famously pebbly beach.

Ten-year-old Doreen, a local girl, is amongst hundreds of happy holidaymakers having a paddle in the sea near the West End Café in Hove, with her brother, her sister and two school friends. Others have decided that mere paddling won't suffice, and have taken to the water. Several people are in a rowing boat between the two piers, while a teenage girl from West Croydon is canoeing. Much further up the beach, out at sea past the end of Paston Place groyne, a local boatman is enjoying some solitude in his small vessel while, at Black Rock, a party of people are shrimping out on the rocks. It's a tranquil end to a perfect summer's day.

Then, at around 6.30pm, a black ridge appears on the horizon. The few who notice observe it sweeping towards the shore from the south-west. As it nears, there's a roar, and the sky appears to blacken.

A huge wave rears up over the heads of the paddlers and the swimmers, the deckchairs and sunbathers. It travels nearly thirty feet up the beach, carrying all before it. Later, eyewitness estimates of the wave's height will differ – ten feet say some, twenty feet according to others – but it washes up to the high tide level.

Boats on the water are spun round, bathers bob like corks and paddlers are knocked off their feet. People sitting in deckchairs suddenly find themselves waist-deep in water, and the sea around them is now littered with deckchairs and clothes, bags and towels, buckets and spades.

The wave carries the boatman near Paston Place groyne up the sand and along the beach; he eventually comes to rest, wedged against the promenade wall, under the Volk's Railway. The occupants of the rowing boat between the piers have to scramble for safety when it capsizes near the shore. The canoeing day-tripper from West Croydon finds herself riding the wave up the beach, her paddle wrenched from her hands by the sheer force of the water. The canoe overturns and she is dashed on to the stones. Her bathing costume is torn and her arms and shoulders badly bruised. She is rescued by several men who run along a groyne and drag her to safety. The Black Rock shrimpers are also left bruised and cut when the wave knocks them off their feet and they flounder to safety.

Then a second wave hits, sucking the sand bone-dry and taking debris with it. It curls against the beach and rears right over the heads of bathing-station attendants who are rescuing those hit by the first wave. The backwash around the groynes appears to be boiling. And then, almost before anyone has time to comprehend what has happened, torrential rain starts to pour, drenching the already-soaked and shocked crowds. Having escaped the wave, they now scamper into shop doorways and seafront shelters. Others give up completely and head for their boarding houses and hotels.

Miraculously, it seems that no one is killed or seriously injured. However, twenty-four hours later, a young woman's body, clad only in underclothes, is washed up by the sea at the foot of the cliffs at Rottingdean. Later identified as twenty-seven-year-old Annie Simmons, she has a head wound and bruises on her face and shoulders which, along with her scanty attire, indicate she was Brighton and Hove's only fatality of the wave.

Others on the South Coast beaches are not so fortunate. At Folkstone, a twelve-foot wave – the first of eight – rushes along the beach and into the harbour. Several motor-boats at its mouth are swept two hundred yards into the inner harbour. Sixteen-year-old Arthur Balkham, a local boy who was fishing on the breakwater on the west side of Harbour Pier, is washed away by the first wave. Only the cap he was wearing is found. In Hastings, Mrs Lilian Pollard from Woking, one of four people on a fishing expedition, drowns when a twenty-foot wave capsizes the boat she is in. At Worthing, the sea churns up a six-foot wave which sweeps rapidly into shore. Within five minutes the sea rises from low to half-full tide. And, perhaps most significantly, on the east side of the Isle of Wight, a bank of sand sweeps along the seafront with enough force to over-turn boats on Sandown beach.

The coroner at the inquest into the death of Lilian Pollard remarks, 'The great wave was unaccountable.' However, in his quest to find fault, the coroner ignores the obvious faults. Perhaps he's never heard of Wight-Bray. Perhaps you haven't.

Wight-Bray is an undersea transcurrent fault, which means whenever its two sides have moved, they have done so in different horizontal directions, rather than vertically. Wight-Bray slices its way south-east across the English Channel, passing under the Isle of Wight and down to the coast of France, just north of Eawy. The fault was most active during the Jurassic period, but there is no geological evidence to suggest that its moving days are done for good. And Wight-Bray has a smaller, but perfectly formed neigh-bour; stretching out offshore from Christchurch Bay, also in a south-easterly direction, is the Christchurch fault. So, if you stand on Brighton beach and look to the south-west, averting your gaze from Worthing, you're facing the fault-lines of Christchurch and Wight-Bray.

Some Brightonians know where the fault lies. Argus reader Denise Bennett from Portslade was only six months old when her family nar-rowly escaped harm on 20th July 1929. Writing to the paper in 2001, she says she understood the wave was caused by *an earth tremor on the Chichester Fault*. Someone's memory was obviously slight faulty but 'Chichester' instead of 'Christchurch' is close enough.

I Was Sure the Waves Would Kill Me.

I put The Argus back in my bag, and take a long look towards the south-west. I wonder when my nightmare will come again.

Moment 4:
The Mugging
by Katy Gardner

He's watching me. As I reach the crest of the hill, I sense his gaze. Not curious or even impatient, he knows what he wants, and he's prepared to wait. For a moment I pause on the pavement, catching my breath as I take in the view: the large sky with its skittering, uncertain clouds, the hospital towers to the East, and, directly below, the gaudy promise of the pier. Today the sea is restless. Even from here I can see the flicks of foam and, further out, the shadows of the racing clouds. We've already spent an hour on the beach, tossing pebbles at the waves. Then to Boots for nappies and back, past the junkies on St James's Street and further up the hill towards the park, these maternity-leave mornings eked out by small shapeless chores.

The climb has made me sticky. Kicking on the buggy's brake, I pull off my jacket and add it to the mound of shopping that's balanced on the back. Here's one more thing I never knew about mumsy-ville: the gug and goo that covers one 24/7, from the small pools of baby posset drying on my shoulders to the sudden soak of milk spreading, embarrassingly, from my bust. And then the hot flushes caused by all this buggy-pushing, up and down the hills of Brighton.

What I need is a sit-down and a piece of cake. I'm going to ignore the predatory presence in the trees. I am going to join the vigil around the sandpit, taking my place amongst the other mothers, who, numbingly bored, stare into space as their toddlers shovel sand into plastic cups, or whisper into their mobiles, their snoozing babies clamped to their tits.

After ten minutes of shouting, followed by the dwindling whine of encroaching sleep, my own little darling has collapsed against the cushions of her vehicle. Manoeuvring it past the dog shit and through the gate, I push the buggy down the grassy hummock towards the café. Different groups of mums cluster around the plastic tables, the social morphology of the city in miniature: the

Queen's Park types with their Overlander prams and corduroy slings, feeding their infants organic mush on their way back from baby yoga; the girls from the Bristol Estate, with their piercings and Burberry-edged three-wheelers, their shaven headed toddlers and pink frilled babies. A lone Bangladeshi woman is pushing her child on the swings. When I smile at her, she looks away. On the benches next to the climbing frame, a large, unhappy looking woman takes a drag on her ciggie. I've noticed her here before with her lumbering, overweight kids. Last week she was rounded on by the Queen's Park lot because her oldest lad was throwing sand.

Okay. I've arrived at the kiosk. I'm going to forget about what happened last week. I'm going to see this through. Parking my daughter by one of the tables, I finger the coins in my pocket. A mug of tea and a plate of sandwiches. Is that too much to ask? Yet, as I pay for my lunch, I sense his presence again, a flicker of movement in the corner of my vision, my stalker returned. He doesn't want to be seen so when I glance round he has vanished. Yet, just like at the top of the hill, I know he's somewhere close, watching and waiting. Picking up the tea with one hand and the plate of sandwiches with the other, I turn around.

That's when it happens. I thought that, in the short distance between kiosk and table, I would survive. I thought I'd be quick with my defences, not another victim of the Queen's Park muggings. Yet, as I step towards my baby's buggy, I am ambushed. There's a rush of something white and, with precision, the plate is knocked from my hand. As I jolt backwards, tea arcs from my mug, splattering the queue. It's then that I scream, a sharp yelp of distress that causes the other mothers to stop mid-sentence and turn in alarm, like watchful meerkats about to dart for cover.

I've been attacked, targeted with ruthless efficiency, done over once more. As my empty plate crashes to the ground, the seagull swoops back to his perch on the kiosk roof. His cold, yellow eyes are already identifying new victims. Mulching the bread in his cruel beak, he gobbles down my lunch.

Moment 5:
An Afternoon
by Marian Garvey

It is the third lay-by they have parked in, this time bang up against a hedge. When her mother unwinds the window, fuchsia bursts in and the leaves spring into the car which is already stuffed tight with August heat.

For Agnes Byrne, who's spent the last two hours with her mother and sister in a car from London to Brighton, the prancing flowers are too much to endure. So she leans across her mother and winds the window back up again. A few of the flowers fall, into her mother's lap.

'You've killed them,' whines Lucy from the back.

'They're flowers,' says Agnes, turning to slap at her sister's sprawling legs.

'She hit me mum!'

'Girls,' sighs their mother, handing the broken flowers to Lucy. Lucy crying, 'You've killed them. You've killed them.'

'Time to get out.' Their mother sighs again, tries opening her door against the heat, but it won't budge, hemmed in by the weight of the hedge. All three look towards the passenger side.

'Is that the house Mum?' Lucy squashed now between the front seats, chewing penny sweets.

'Better be,' says Agnes, watches the side of Lucy's face as she chews and chews. Agnes wants some of the strawberry-ness.

The bungalow, one of three, is set back on the opposite side of the road. They have been built for the view of the sea. From the middle house comes the sound of young children. A seesaw is stretched across the front garden, its metal creaking with the weight and laughing of them, their hysteria coming in snatches. They are standing with their arms about each other trying to stay balanced.

'There'll be an accident!' That sigh again.

'Oh mum!' Agnes wants to cry suddenly, wants to be on the seesaw, to be one of the young girls laughing and screeching, not in a hired Fiesta with her mother leaning over her shoulder. A dog

22

Moments 6-12:

<u>Moment 6:</u>
Baked Beans on Concrete
by Will Ainley

<u>**Moment 7:**</u>
Plays Dirty
by Paul Burgess

Moment 8:
Eubank Moment
by Graham Carter

<u>Moment 9:</u>
The World Beard and
Moustache Championship
by Astrid Chesney

<u>Moment 10:</u>
West Pier Starlings
by Miles Donovan

Moment 11:
The Hove Moment
by Peter James Field

THE HOVE MOMENT.

<u>Moment 12:</u>
Squirrel Death
by David Foldvari

barks, this time from the end house. The discordant howling splits the afternoon.

'Sounds like a wolf!' says Lucy.

'Don't be stupid,' Agnes says, but scans the houses all the same. It is such a terrible noise. The laughing from the seesaw has turned to fighting and crying, accusations and screeches. A woman runs out shouting and the kids are rushed inside.

When Agnes opens the door of the car it is onto silence. 'This is the last house mum. If she's not here, we're going to the beach.'

They get out, the girls easily enough but they have to pull at their mother as she squeezes from the driver's seat over to the passenger one. She gets stuck. She's having difficulty lifting her leg and they're all laughing.

'I'm doing a wee, I'm doing a wee,' says Lucy.

'You dare...,' but the urine is already splattering the hot tar, catching Agnes's pale calves.

'Gross!' says Agnes trying to wipe it off, with a clutch of Lucy's skirt, the frilly material moving further and further down the little girl's legs, Lucy squealing.

'STOP THAT!' says their mother, out of the car now. 'Come on Lucy, you'll have to put your swimsuit on. It's in the boot.' And Agnes watches as they hustle to the back of the car where they're hidden from view.

She looks around. There are bungalows everywhere, raked in snaking roads up the hill, and when she stands on tiptoe, convinced she'll be able to see the Marina they've just driven past, all she can see are the tops of yet more bungalows, neatly curving in and out, all the way down the hill.

She likes the warm air, the breeze that wraps round her. She leans back against the bonnet of the car and closes her eyes against the sun. She thinks she can hear the tinkling rattle of sails from the boats in the dock, remembers the last time they'd come and they'd walked around it, her dad pointing out the different sails, the main-stay, the jib, Lucy telling him that she didn't want a boat with sails, she wanted a boat with a key, her father swinging her up onto his shoulders laughing, 'Does madam Lucy mean a gin palace!'

It is quiet except for her mother's murmured coaxing as she helps Lucy dress. When Lucy reappears, all flowery in a bathing suit over which is another cotton skirt, Agnes thinks she looks quite sweet but can't resist telling her she still smells of piss.

The young girl cries, 'She swore again mum!'

Their mother slams the boot shut, making the girls jump. And they cross over the road in silence.

There is something not quite right about the house. It stands neat and well-kept, the type of house Agnes's mother calls 'a fine house.' All three stand in front of the gate till Lucy moves forward to open it. She fiddles with the latch. It is tied with something and their mother bends down to help unwind it. Agnes watches them together, intent on their task together, can't bear their quiet concentration. She suddenly wants to shove them into the gate and walk away by herself. By herself. Down to the sea.

When her mother had got this day-trip into her head – 'We can look up Sheila, she's an old teaching friend,' Lucy squawking, 'Yeah, the seaside, the seaside!' – the only reason Agnes had agreed to come was to go to the beach to see the sea .

The first time they'd ever come, years ago, she'd been so excited. They'd parked the car in one of those underground carparks and walked under the road through a smelly tunnel. She remembers that it didn't matter because at the end it opened up on to light and sky and she could see the sea. It had taken a while to realise that the beach was full of pebbles, and she and Lucy had tried and tried to build a sandcastle. Lucy crying 'Daddy it won't stick! It won't stick!' and he'd taken them down to the water's edge, showed them how to skim stones. Lucy had just lifted up huge rocks and chucked them in at her feet.

And today, when they'd finally got here, through all the traffic, they'd had to drive the length of the seafront in one direction before her mother had nearly killed them doing a U-turn, asking Agnes to check the address yet again, insisting, 'It's out of town we should be heading,' and Agnes could hardly bear it, *out of town* being as good as the day was going to get. She had even agreed with Lucy about going on the pier. Lucy with her nose against the window, 'Look! Mum it's even got a helter skelter!' but then they'd driven the length of the seafront, in the other direction as if they were in some motorcade with their mother pointing out the white houses from 'Oliver' and Lucy going 'Really mum? From the film, from the film?' Agnes wondering why Sheila couldn't live in one of these 'film houses' instead of Salt Dean or whatever dean she lived in.

Lucy hadn't even turned her face towards the sea, seen the miles of sky blue railings on the other side of the road holding back the blueness. Her mother hadn't looked either, too busy concentrating on driving the car. And this had stopped Agnes from being able to see it. You would think you couldn't miss it, all that blue. But every time she'd looked, the sea had melded with the haze of the sky and there was no horizon.

'Why are you crying?' Lucy's hot little hand on her arm. The gate standing open.

'Because the sun... the sun's in my eyes stupid.' Lucy looking at their mother who gives Agnes a look but says nothing, just holds Lucy's hand.

Her mother tries to put the other hand round Agnes's shoulder but Agnes slips from under it.

'It's hot,' she says, and walks ahead of them through the gate.

The front garden is paved and full of tall rose bushes that mark the way to the door. The smell makes Agnes feel sick. Agnes waits for her mother to comment, roses are her favourite flower, but her mother is not looking at the flowers, she is looking at where Lucy is pointing. At a dog. The great underside of dog, an Alsatian that tracks them with its eyes as they move up the garden path. It is behind the bay window, sitting half on the window sill, and half on what looks like the back of a sofa. The curtains are pulled over so it looks like a puppet, popping its head out before the show begins. The dog is whining, in a weak, given-up sort of way, a noise that is too small for its body. They can hardly hear it because of the double-glazing, but its slobber smears the window and it scratches and paws at the glass, showing the red swollen teats on its underbelly.

'What's the matter with the dog mum?' Lucy looks towards their mother but she's not listening, she's concentrating on the front door.

'Ah! Hello, Sheila.'

The woman is holding roses and the darkness falls in the hall behind, casting her like a statue in shadow. She doesn't seem to hear the greeting but instead concentrates on her hand which is pricked with tiny drops of blood. 'Hold these would you, there's a good girl.' Agnes can do nothing but accept the briary stems. Then the woman turns to Agnes's mother. 'I thought I heard voices, I said to Larry, he's busy at the garden, I can hear something and he told me you're always hearing something, Sheila, and I am of course, only this time I was right, you're very welcome, Maura and the girls of course, are these the girls? They've got so big. Christ, time flies, doesn't it? I wouldn't know them, or you for that matter, you're looking great,

41

come in, come in you must be baked, did you drive down or train? The drive's nice, come in we'll sit in the garden and have tea, I'm so glad you're here. I was talking to Joan and she said you might call. We're on the phone, Larry likes people to phone, but no matter, a great surprise.'

They step across the threshold into the darkness. Agnes's palms hurt because she has closed her hands too tightly on the thorny stems. When she opens them one of the flowers falls on the carpet. 'Oohh don't let them fall, they're Larry's best. He'll be cross and then where would we be?'

'What's wrong with the dog?'

'Shh Lucy,' says their mother, nudging her to be quiet.

The woman turns and smiles, her pretty face grey beneath her tan.

'The dog wants to be out. She's not happy, but Larry's at the garden. You know the way,' and, 'I'll take those shall I?' indicating the roses.

Agnes gives them to her and the woman walks over to a small polished table and puts them in a crystal vase. There are petals on the patterned carpet and Agnes bends down to pick them up, but the woman walks through them.

'Leave them pet, there's more to be doing than bothering about petals.'

She shuts the front door and the outside heat is suddenly far away. Fresh. Beyond breathing. This is a new heat. A false heat that radiates from the florals of the wallpaper, the carpet, the curtains, everything. Everything, holding and hogging and trapping the heat.

The woman opens a door. It's the room the dog is in and it bounds towards them, baying, and the woman closes the door against it just in time.

'That's not fair!' Lucy nudged again by her mother.

'It's not fair and she's not happy but she's alright for now,' the woman says, smiling at Lucy. 'She wants to go out into the garden, that's all.'

'Why can't she then? Maybe she's too hot, maybe that's why she's crying, we heard her outside.'

Again the smile, and this time a sigh. Agnes recognises it. It sounds like her mother's sighs. 'The thing is pet... We can't always have what we want.'

Immediately the woman begins to fret and she turns to Agnes's mother.

42

'If I'd known you were coming, Maura, I'd have…'

'Don't worry,' says Agnes's mother. 'We just popped in.' But the woman doesn't seem to hear this.

'Now, where to start?' and she begins to pace the small hall.

She runs the tips of her fingers over and over her mouth, tenderly, almost. Agnes doesn't know why she wants the woman to bite them. The dog is whining quietly behind the door and Lucy looks stricken. Agnes moves over to stand next to her. The woman is leaning with her hand on the table the flowers are on. She is muttering about the house and her mother is speaking softly to her, 'Sheila, don't worry about it.' She's using the same voice she used with Lucy outside at the car and the other woman is listening and speaking at the same time. 'What have we all come to Maura? You… and the poor girls… Larry and that garden… it's all he does.' And Agnes's mother is patting her arm.

Agnes knows this voice, the voice the woman is using. It is a voice that Agnes has come to know well. It is the voice they all use in their house now.

Lucy is staring, her mother staring, Lucy asking, 'Agnes are you crying?' and the woman calls out, 'Oh you poor, poor girls!' rushes over, is kneeling in front of them, clutching and squeezing them together, her arms around them both, her head buried in their fresh clothes. She smells of drink.

'I want to go home.' Lucy alarmed. The woman is heavy, and all three of them are falling slowly sideways, against the wall, without noise. 'Mum!' mouths Agnes, eyeballing her mother above the woman's head.

'Where shall we start Sheila?' and her mother picks the woman up, like an expert 'Are these the bedrooms?' leading the way down the stifling corridor. Agnes and Lucy getting to their feet following, into the gloom, Agnes holding Lucy's hand. Lucy making her she's-weird face, Agnes pinching her nose, pointing at the woman, their mother turning, giving them one of her looks.

The bedrooms are all the same. Dark, with the curtains drawn, sparse, twin beds, maybe a chest of drawers. And this they only know from the descriptions the woman gives. She stands in the doorway, her arm leaning on Agnes's mother, breathing heavily. There is hardly room for anyone else. She tells them where she bought the wallpaper, the carpets, what furniture they brought from London, turns unexpectedly, catching the girls making faces, asks them sharply, 'Will you be going to Ireland for your holidays?' And when they say yes, 'And which do you prefer, England or Ireland?' Agnes and Lucy looking at each other. They are used to this from their mother's friends.

'Ireland,' they say in unison.

After the tour Agnes whispers to her mother about leaving but Sheila is already talking about Agnes helping her make the tea. 'You put out the cups on the tray like a good girl.' Lucy and their mother sent out into the sun. Though the kitchen is dark, like the rest of the house, the Venetian blinds let in little chinks of light and through the open back door Agnes can see a sloping lawn and, beyond the hedge, the blue of the sea.

She feels energetic suddenly, starts talking about school, about her friends, the end of term disco, which was embarrassing but okay. She lays out the little china cups on the saucers and she likes the feel of the smooth porcelain. She watches Sheila leaning against the counter waiting for the kettle to boil, the sun from the open door on her face and she tells her about how they came by car not train. She tells her about the stupid hire car, a total rip-off with its wind-down window and no air-conditioning. She tells her how she pointed this out to her mother, that they had a perfectly good car in the garage and how her mother had said calmly that it was an automatic, that Daddy had always done the driving, and didn't Agnes know she hadn't driven in years and it was hard enough going back to it without worrying about windows. That, in the scheme of things, car windows were the least of her worries. And how she'd screamed at her mother, what about *her* scheme? Did her mother not know that she also had a scheme? And Sheila smiles, wets the tea.

And Agnes tells her how her mum had taken the car out twice with the man from the rental place, how Agnes had asked her, 'Did she fancy him or what?' or maybe he fancied her mother which was disgusting because her mum was old and she looked terrible and when she'd said all this to her mother, who'd been sitting at the kitchen table marking books, she'd left out the bit about her mother looking old and terrible because her mother did look old and terrible and what made her look even worse was all the smiling she'd started doing, all those funny smiles that weren't smiles at all, just sad creases in her face but then her mum had smiled and the smile had turned into laughing and more laughing till Agnes had kept saying, 'What? *What?*' and her mother had told her about the time

44

when Granddad had died in Derry, how Granny was in the office at the coal yard when this customer came in and put up a bag of grapes on the counter and Granny had thought that he was there to pay his condolences and his bill. But he was there because he wanted to know would she walk out with him and when Granny had realised what he was saying to her, Granny had said, 'Oh no! No!' and then the man had snatched back the bag of grapes and gone out with a puss on him that would stop a clock.

Sheila bent over the counter roaring, laughing, and Agnes laughing, saying, 'And I said, is that going to happen to you, Mum? Is the car rental man going to give you a bag of grapes?'

Sheila brings over the teapot, puts it on the tray. She calls Agnes *good* and *girl*, touches her hair, asks her to get the milk from the fridge.

Agnes is turning back towards her, holding the milk bottle, when she sees Sheila swig from the little flag of whisky that she is putting to the back of the cupboard.

The garden is huge. Agnes blinks at Lucy running in the sunlight towards her. 'Look Agnes look!' And Agnes looks at Lucy spinning, gulls wheeling in the air above her. She's cartwheeling over the lawn, her arms and legs flinging in all directions as if they are hardly attached to her. She's dancing and laughing, calling to them all 'Come on Mum! Agnes come on! Sheila!' and she has them all laughing back at her.

Agnes closes one eye to see better: Lucy's bare feet on the green grass, her thin arms swaying in the blue air and, over the top of her head, between the tiled roofs of bungalows, Agnes sees the sea. The white-blueness in the distance, dropping into the sky.

Agnes and Lucy have flopped on the grass, against their mother, when Sheila calls out to Larry about tea. They only realise there's a gap in the hedge when Larry moves through it.

'A secret garden!' Lucy's on her feet. 'Can we see it? Can we see it?' Already running down the length of the garden, Sheila shouting to Larry not to let the child through, Larry shouting about people having no manners, that they should call, that when you live by the sea, people are like a rash, all over you, and Agnes is amazed. Her mother is starting to run. After Lucy. She can't remember the last time her mother ran.

And so she begins to run too. Sheila is screaming at them to come back. 'Not there! Not there!' But Lucy is already through the gap.

Beyond the gap it is wild. Agnes and her mother stand still. They cannot run, the grass is too tall. It reaches their knees, dark swishes, lighter at the tips bleached by the sun.

Lucy is near the bottom of the garden. She is half as tall again as the grass. She stands straight, her neck bent down looking at something. All Agnes can hear is the soft sound of the grass as she and her mother move through it. When they reach her, Lucy doesn't turn her head to look at them. On the ground the grass has been flattened. There is an aluminium pail and next to it lie four puppies. They are lying on their left sides, placed there gently by someone. There is no breeze.

Moment 13:
I Live in Just the Right Place
by Annabel Giles

If I move in an easterly direction from my house I will soon find myself in Kemp Town village, home of the homosexual gift shop and over-priced banana. Closing my eyes as I pass the Marina (soon to be corrupted into something even less worth looking at) and giant super-store Chavda, on most sunny mornings I cycle with my son along the undercliff path to his pirates' school in Rottingdean. If I had any legs left after that, I could carry on up the hill and down again to the retro Saltdean Lido, where I would fully expect to see retro people from their retro housing heavy retro petting. After that it's Eastbourne, which I haven't yet visited because I'm too young. Just.

Should I decide to leave my home and head north, I am liable to be run over by a speeding Shopmobility scooter for the disabled from the sheltered housing estate opposite, hurtling round the corner on one wheel. I have even seen them racing each other. Down the middle of the road, in the dark, with no lights. Which may explain how they got to own such vehicles in the first place.

Having walked for a good ten minutes past all the empty *Disabled* parking spaces to my car, I would proceed at precisely thirty miles an hour (anyone else got twelve points on their licence for driving at a dangerous thirty-six mph and once, but only once, at thirty-seven?) through Hanover (tiny houses, huge hair), past the perfectly preserved 1940s rockery at Preston Park, and then on up the motorway to what used to be London, but is now Eastern Europe. Turning straight round and coming back down again, I will smile as I whizz – slowly – past the tall stone pillars which used to say *Dirty Weekend* but now shout *Nearly home!* (My friend David always toots his horn when he passes through them; I tried doing that once but was followed all the way home by a big red man in a small white van.)

Immediately west from my house is 'Doggy Fashion', a grooming parlour not for poodles but proper Brighton 'I-may-look-quite-cute-but-in-fact-I'm-hard-as-fucking-nails' dogs. You can see them in the window, having their hair done, glowering back at you, memorising your face for when they're next off the lead.

Having run the gauntlet of St James's, where the cry on the street is 'oo's nicked me meffadone you fuckin' fuckahs?', I feel more amongst my people as I pass the Royal Pavilion, surely the biggest, most beautiful girls' blouse in all of Brighton. And they do jolly nice cake in the tea-room. Must remember to get married there next time.

The North Laine is for us residents; the Brighton Lanes are for them tourists. We love the independently spirited shops staffed mainly by individuals with interesting haircuts; they love their giant chain stores stuffed into tiny spaces. But each religion lives happily side by side as they both celebrate the same festivals, and we're all happy shoppers.

Let's pretend that Churchill Square doesn't exist.

Hove, despite its recent attempts to bitch itself up, is still very naice. The streets are clean, everything is in order. Always a parking space to be found, lots of painted white woodwork, all dogs kept on a lead. Life just as it should be.

And on the seafront, neat rows of beach huts, natty nylon chairs and pop-up picnic tables. The good people of Hove, however, unable to think of an imaginative name for a café that would be a good place to meet

You can spot the Hove housewife at fifty paces: designer messy, leather jacket atop a tutu, spits on Victoria Beckham, brightly coloured sofas and large paper lamp-globes at home. Usually accompanied by a boy child with long wavy hair, called something like Spike, his little sister Ludmilla resplendent in matted ratstails and a sexier outfit than Mummy's.

If I head south, I don't go very far at all. It takes ages to cross Madeira Drive because the traffic's going too slowly, but just past the Argus readers still picking through the stones looking for Fatboy Slim's broken glass, there it is. The sea. Glorious, magnificent, all-powerful. Bigger than me, wider than you, best friends with the sky. God's property. The reason we're here.

Yes, I live in just the right place.

Moment 14:
The Library Sign
by Peter Guttridge

I figured today was the perfect day for me to get a sign. I wasn't looking for anything major: Brighton's male cyclists suddenly turning less belligerent or local football supporters saying it was wrong to wreck an area of outstanding natural beauty just to build a sports stadium. File those under 'Miracles' anyway.

My sign would be more personal, more to do with the fact I hadn't had a book published for three years or written anything for four. Although that wasn't necessarily personal. According to Mallarmé, books are all-encompassing. *Everything in the world exists to end up in a book*, he said. Yes, that's got me beat too.

I ignored the Queen of Hearts canoodling with the Mad Hatter on a bench glowing green in Jubilee Square. I pushed through the crowds of people milling in the cold sunshine. I ignored the score of more-successful-than-me writers squashed together for a photo-call in front of the huge wall of glass.

Today was a triple whammy: the long-awaited opening of Brighton's new central library; World Book Day; and the launch of Brighton Reads, a project to encourage as many people as possible to read Lewis Carroll's Alice's Adventures in Wonderland.

'Surely this is the perfect day for my sign,' I muttered, pushing a gangly White Rabbit out of the way to get into the library. Something that would indicate what I should do.

I'd had a great idea for a novel for the past four years; I just hadn't been able to write a page of it.

There was a useless piece of information rattling round in my head that had something to do with it. Did you know that Harvard's library has five million books on fifty-seven miles of shelves? You do now. Since I'd heard that, I'd wondered what was the point of adding my flimsy effort to the pile.

It was bad enough going into the bookshops in town and seeing shelf after shelf of fiction. Sure, I still went to the section where the remains of my backlist was housed and turned the covers face out to attract more attention but that was just basic writer's reflex.

In the library foyer I sidestepped two bickering Alices and a Humpty Dumpty whose eyes begged me to intercede. I passed on into the body of the library, hurrying past books and more bloody books.

The library staff had been encouraged to dress up as famous writers. I skirted a passable Shakespeare – noting that not every man has the legs for hose, even in Brighton – and a man I took to be Charles Dickens. On a second look I recognised him and realised his beard was just because he lived in Lewes.

I was thrown by the sight of a man and a woman standing together in ordinary clothes with some kind of napkins draped over their heads and necks. They saw my puzzlement and said together:

'The Barretts of Wimple Street.'

I could still hear their giggles when I reached the public loos in the far corner of the library. The public toilets in this eco-friendly glass and steel cathedral of knowledge (I'm quoting again) used rainwater sluiced from the roof for the flush. Alas, we were in the middle of a drought. The sign on the door said *Out of Order*, which I didn't necessarily take as personally indicative.

This long-awaited library opening was not without such setbacks. The sophisticated solar panel and air-vent system that regulated temperature wasn't so sophisticated after all. Over the past two pre-opening weeks, depending on where they were in the library, staff had discovered they either steamed or froze. Some claimed to have seen penguins on the top floor but that probably just reflected council staffing policy.

The lifts up to the mezzanine and top floor had broken first thing this morning. Rumour had it the mayor and other dignitaries were trapped inside them. Cruel people hoped so. 'Hope is the thing with feathers,' someone announced, quoting Emily Dickinson. Can't help you with that one either.

There were a few hundred people in the square. For reasons of Health and Safety, they were only being allowed ingress in dribs and – definitely – drabs. A number thought they might return the next day, the second day of the library's long-awaited opening. Except the next day was a Wednesday and all libraries in the city closed on a Wednesday. The council was spending a fortune to attract people to a new library that would be closed on its second day of opening.

I figured there were staff toilets in the basement so headed that way, taking the stairs two at a time, down, down and, well, down. I was soon in the bowels of the building but apparently no nearer a toilet. Instead, there was an old wooden door, scabbed with peeling paint.

I rattled the door handle and pushed. Nothing. I turned to retrace my steps and heard a dreadful creaking. I turned back, aware, as the door swung open, I was probably now officially a character in a Stephen King novel.

I walked into a vast, dimly lit room. I could see other rooms radiating from it to right and left. Every wall was layered with bookshelves from floor to high ceiling.

I approached a tall desk behind which a large old man hunched. I wondered who he was meant to be.

'The universe – which others call the library – is composed of an indefinite and perhaps infinite number of hexagonal galleries,' he said, making the tiniest waving gesture at the room with his left hand. Not a Stephen King novel, then.

'Thanks for that,' I said. Adding under my breath: 'Mr Borges.'

I know a blind Argentinian librarian when I see one.

'Don't suppose there's a loo here?'

He looked down at me with unseeing eyes.

'There are books. An indefinite – perhaps infinite – number.'

'Yeah, I got that,' I said, looking at the bookshelves to my left. Oddly, in the gloom, I couldn't actually make out any books on them. As I attempted to peer closer he said:

'Welcome to the library of books that are not yet written.'

For which, I felt sure, read, in big, bold letters: A SIGN.

'Being librarian here is a curious job but not without its rewards.' He turned the corners of his mouth up. 'Cataloguing is, naturally, a little open-ended.'

I peered at the wall of bookshelves.

'And the shelves a bit bare, I would think,' I said. 'Or is that because all the books have been borrowed?'

He looked sternly down on me.

'This is not a lending library. It's a reference library – one of the best. Researchers come from all over the world to pore over the stock. Our desks are full of scholars making voluminous notes.'

I could see no desks, nor scholars.

He clasped his hands on the desk in front of him.

'There is a palpable excitement in the thought of what books might one day fill these bare shelves,' he said. 'Those not yet written, naturally. Also, books not yet written but which have been begun.

And, best of all, perhaps, those not yet imagined.'

I did a little twirl to take in every shelf-heavy wall, wondering exactly where my idea fitted in. If at all.

'How does that work?' I said. 'Would a book not yet completed but begun ever appear on the shelves? Once begun, surely it would have no place here? Your library is solely for books that haven't yet been written.'

He sighed and lightly squeezed his nose at its narrow tip.

'Actually, the library was originally for books *never* written but the committee appointed to decide our constitution thought that this suggested a certain boastfulness on our part. We argued about it for months. But how could we possibly know with absolute certainty that such and such a book would never be written?'

'Not yet written is more modest, certainly,' I said. 'But I guess it also means that you are forever binning books once they have actually been written.'

'Not as often as you might think,' he said, rubbing his hands together. This man clearly suffered from Method actor syndrome: no fidget too pointless. 'When I started there were occurrences that puzzled me. One of our most prized possessions would go missing. Then I realised this was always because someone, somewhere had been inspired to write it. Some of our most popular works went that way.'

'How did you cope?'

'People do ask what our most prized possession is but we can't play favourites,' he said, ignoring me. He scratched his chin.

'I'll bet.' I was intrigued by the notion of this library but was becoming less certain that it was my sign.

'And people make suggestions to enlarge the stock. Arrogantly: "But you simply must have this book, it's never been written and I doubt ever will be". Diffidently: "I'm sure you've thought of this but there's a book you might want to consider for inclusion. Though I'm sure it won't meet your criteria".'

I nodded. A pointless thing to do in response to a blind person but I was discombobulated.

'I hate to be negative but don't you think there are enough unread books in the world without the need for a library of books that are unread because not yet written? I'm not going to live long enough to reread all the books I have on my shelves at home. Then there are all the books I've never read, all the books I've never wanted to read –'

'All of the books that you haven't written, perhaps?' he said.

I looked at him sharply. He was tugging at his ear now.

'Listen. I do have this idea for a novel. But will I ever write it? Maybe your catalogue can give me a clue – you know, if it's in there then that must mean –'

'We keep the catalogue deliberately skimpy to discourage plagiarism. We wouldn't want two authors not writing the same book.'

I thought about that for a moment then sighed.

'I came in hoping for a sign.'

He jerked his head.

'The toilet sign is over there.'

'Music hall lives,' I said, moving off. No sign for me today then.

He called after me.

'In our biggest but constantly changing section. The one for novels that will probably get written even though there is absolutely no need to write them.'

Moment 15:
Brighton Moment 883
by Carole Hayman

I was lying in the bath when it came to me. I wasn't taking a bath; I was stretched, fully dressed, staring through the uncurtained window. My partner had just remarked that the best thing about the house was that you could see the sea from the bathroom – even better – while actually in the bath. Dutifully I climbed in, boots and all, to test the view.

We'd been looking for a house for a year and were now in the desperate phase where we'd take anything. We nearly bought a flat in Hove, but my partner bottled out. We couldn't live in Hove, he said, people went there to die. Now, having been lied to many times, and once actually gazumped, we were more than weary of Brighton. That morning, the estate agent had called us in London.

I know you never want to speak to me again... hahah... but I think I may have found just what you're looking for. Could you possibly come down today? I know it's gonna be snapped up.

It was a damp, dark February day and there was nothing we fancied less than a miserably wet trek down the M23. But fate will have its way and we went, telling ourselves we'd give it one last go. When we saw the house, on the brow of a hill and bright, beach-hut blue, we were both enchanted.

My partner was right. From the bath I could indeed see the sea. More especially I could see the pier. It was then that I remembered the last time I'd been on it. It was years before.

My best friend, Daragh, was in a relationship swerving dangerously towards Beachy Head. I felt bad for her, wanted to make it better. It was her birthday. She needed a treat, to be entertained, something *special*. A day trip, I thought, and – as she was gay – obviously to Brighton. I remembered there was a rather posh fish restaurant my ex-husband had once taken me to for a row. I called them and booked a table for two for lunch. 'It has to be a nice table,' I said. 'It's a birthday'.

It was a lovely, sharply bright late spring day. All went cheerfully

54

Moments 16-22:

<u>Moment 16:</u>
West Pier RIP
by Jason Ford

<u>Moment 17:</u>
Stormy Morning en Route
to Poynings
by Jasper Goodall

Moment 18:
The Erogenous Zone
by Professor George Hardie

<u>Moment 19:</u>
Day Return to Brighton
by Margaret Huber

<u>Moment 20:</u>
Attempting to Walk Through
The Lanes on a Saturday
by Oliver Hydes

<u>Moment 21:</u>
A Warm Night and a Full Moon
on Brighton Beach,
August 2003
by Joe McLaren

<u>Moment 22:</u>
You Put a Spring in
my Step
by Marine

You put a
spring in
my step ...

as we wandered through the lanes, window shopping, people-watching. We had lattes. I bought Daragh a present: a Swatch watch in dazzling pink. She put it straight on, loving it. Then we arrived at the restaurant. The maitre d' was sniffy: two women, one of them with Doc Martens, a nose ring, and spiky green hair? He showed us to a dark corner. We waited twenty minutes for the waiter, who was obviously surprised when we ordered the most expensive things on the menu: sea bass with all its trimmings, oysters to start, and champagne. I insisted.

The oysters were a bit smelly, the champagne warm. We struggled with the sea bass – the trimmings turned out to be its head and fins – and were both, without saying so, relieved when the (very expensive) meal was over.

As the afternoon had turned gloriously warm, I suggested a walk on the pier. Arm in arm, we sauntered past other couples, Daragh eyeing the girlies. There was a heady smell of sugar and frying fat in the air. Pop music blared enticingly from the rides. We stopped to watch mad people on the Big Dipper. As we stood there, Daragh's face turned the same colour as her hair. She let go of my arm and ran to the railings. She leaned over and threw up mightily. Fifty quid's worth of lunch hit the waves below, just missing a startled bather.

I offered Daragh a tissue, to wipe her mouth, and a bottle of water.

'Phew that's better.' She grunted. 'It was that bloody oyster. I knew it was off as soon as I put it in my mouth.'

'Why didn't you spit it out?'

She looked sheepish.

'Didn't want to upset you. You'd gone to so much trouble.'

I should have charged back to the restaurant and made a scene – nothing I enjoy more to be honest, but not everyone agrees, my partner for instance – and it would have spoiled what was left of her birthday. Instead, we resolutely made merry: splashed in the shallows, lay on the beach ogling beauties, even managed chips on the promenade, later.

Soon after, Daragh fell in love with someone much more suitable.

I laughed when she called to tell me they'd had their 'honeymoon' in Brighton.

'I hope you didn't take her to the fish place,' I said.

'Well,' she chortled. 'In a way, I should have. It was all thanks to that bloody oyster that I moved on. Puking it up was cathartic.'

Ten years later, she and her new love are still together.

I smiled as I lay in the bath. 'Yes,' I called to my partner, who was now measuring the kitchen and wondering about taking down a wall. 'Let's buy it. The view from the bathroom's great.'

Moment 23:
Two Ways of Looking at Crime
by Susanna Jones

I. By the Pier

When Mark came out of prison he was nineteen. He had a small amount of cash, a train ticket and the address of a hostel in West London. His family in Scotland, when contacted by the prison, had informed them they didn't want Mark to come home again. He'd gone from a tiny village by the sea to a prison in the countryside. He'd never been to London before and had no idea how to begin looking for the hostel. It was February and the sky was all rain and sleet.

He slept rough for a few weeks near Victoria Coach Station and scrounged enough money for a bus ticket to Eastbourne where someone had told him his cousin might be living. On the day he left London he was tired and his head was groggy with all that had happened in the last two years. Two weeks after his mother's death and a month before Mark was due to join the army, he was involved in a robbery. Before that day he hadn't so much as shoplifted a Mars Bar. Now he was a serious criminal and he was still getting used to himself, and to the thing he had done. His eyelids swollen and sight too blurry to read signs now, he asked someone the way to the bus for Eastbourne. He couldn't hear the directions well but the driver of a bus nearby called to him, 'Off to the seaside mate? Hop on board.' Mark sat next to a middle-aged woman in a voluminous brown fur coat. When the bus slipped out of London, into green fields, he nodded off.

He woke to warmth and softness. In his sleep he had leaned against the fur coat and buried his face in its folds, but the woman didn't seem to mind for when he lifted his head, she smiled. He felt more rested than he had for years. He heard seagulls crying. The bus had stopped. The sky was darkening. 'Are we here?' he asked.

'Final destination,' said the coach driver.

Mark climbed off the bus, knowing already that he would never find his cousin, nor really wanted to. All he knew about Eastbourne was that it had a pier. He could see it already. He left the bus station and crossed the busy road to the promenade. It was all bigger and brighter than he expected Eastbourne to be. Teenage boys and girls swaggered in both directions, chatting, giggling. Mark moved out of their way. When he stood at the railing and looked out to sea, he was confused. There was a second pier just a little further along. The one beside him was light and seemed to dance above the water, the other was darker, closed-up. And then he remembered the coach station, how he had chosen the bus headed for the seaside, how there might have been more than one.

Mark told me this story from a distance of fifteen years and about fifty metres. We were playing air hockey on the Palace Pier one Saturday evening waiting for the rain to pass.

'What did you do that night?' I asked him, as he won his fourth game in succession.

'I slept in a park. My first home in Brighton. Bit cold.'

I thought of the flat Mark lived in now: warm, always spotless, one or two of his own paintings lying around before he'd sell them for good money.

We bought bags of chips, ate them on the prom. 'They're better in the north,' I said, just as Mark said, 'They're better in Scotland' but we kept eating the salty chips as Brighton rolled past in buses, on bicycles, skateboards, and then in a long pink limo.

We stood in silence for a few moments, listened to the sea.

A posse of life-sized Barbie dolls with angel wings came shrieking towards us. One grabbed Mark by his sleeve and swung him around. 'You'll come to my hotel room tonight won't you, Brighton boy?' she laughed. Mark, tall, and strong from years of manual work, was no match for this small plump woman, super-powered, as she was, by euphoria and appetite. He fell to the ground, laughing, and his chips went flying. 'Sorry,' said her friend. 'But you don't know how happy we are.' The hen party clopped away, bare-legged in the cold, off to make more mischief elsewhere in the city.

Mark was still on the ground.

I offered my hand to help him up. He grasped my fingers but stayed on the pavement. Across the road a National Express bus was pulling out of Poole Valley.

'I wish I could tell him,' Mark said.

'Tell who, what?'

'That nineteen-year-old kid on the bus who didn't know where he was. Tell him that it would be all right. That some mistakes are ok.'

II. The Charity Shop

The shoplifter was one of our most regular customers. For that matter, he was one of our most regular shoplifters. We had plenty. We wondered whether, since it was a charity bookshop, people who wouldn't steal from normal shops felt that it was quite all right to pop in and help themselves when they were in need. For most it was just the odd *Dr Who* video or *Guide to English Country Churches* but some were more ambitious. There was the guy who brought his mobile phone to the music section and texted details of our stock to some remote controller who told him which ones to pilfer. Another one somehow distracted the attention of the volunteer at the till and escaped with the emergency appeal collection box under his arm. Perhaps he thought he could get the forty quid's worth of 2p's to Darfur faster than the relief vehicles could. For panache, you couldn't beat the soft-skinned young man who arrived as a new volunteer and walked off in his first afternoon taking not only the contents of the till drawer – several hundred pounds – but also the till drawer. That time we should have seen it coming; his name, he told us, was Robin.

But the person who became known to us simply as 'the shoplifter' had less pizzazz, was more persistent. An artist's impression in the shop daybook showed an unassuming man with smooth black hair under a baseball cap. He was short with a wobbly beer gut. He had a tattoo. He wore a coat on top of another coat, each with large, baggy pockets. He knew that we had different volunteers in the shop every half day and it would take us a while to catch on. We did, but by the time we worked out that all the shoplifters with spider tattoos and blue baseball caps were the same person, half the stock was gone. The shop managers kicked him out at least twice but he always came back.

The day I first saw him, the shop was quiet. I was on my own at the till. I recognised him from the picture as soon as he appeared in the doorway. Since there was no one else around, I thought I'd better keep an eye on him. He moved close to the books in the art section, fiddled with his coat pockets. I watched his hands. Some of those books were expensive.

'How much will you give me for these, darling?'

I jumped. A small doll-like woman with a floppy hat and badly rouged cheeks grabbed my wrist. With her free hand she plonked some tea-stained books about Brighton history on the counter.

'I'm sorry. We can only take donations. It's a charity shop.' I smiled and struggled to free my wrist. I tried to see past her to the art section but her face came closer to mine.

'If you're a charity,' she sprayed, 'let me sell my books. I need the money.'

Then she bounced to the centre of the shop, held her books up high. 'A pound each,' she rasped. 'Who wants to buy?'

A small crowd formed. I could no longer see the baseball cap. Someone gave her 50p for a book of maps. Eventually the group cleared and I saw the cap poking out behind the music stand. The floppy hat moved in next to it.

'Look at this,' the woman sighed to the man. 'The Beatles. I used to like this record. It's a lovely picture.'

'Uh,' he said, then headed out of the shop. He gave me a smug smile as he left. He knew I'd missed my chance.

The woman came to the till and rapped on the counter with a pile of CDs. Her rouge glistened.

'Here you are. No, I'm not buying them. That man with the funny hat was trying to steal them. And this a charity shop.'

I gawped. 'How did you get them off him?'

She screwed up her mouth and stared, apparently insulted. 'He might think he's good but I've been picking pockets for years. Now I'd like a couple of quid for my books please.'

When she left, I watched her in the sunny street, head held high on her tiny frame as she wove through the shoppers. A couple of kids sat on the pavement outside and began to sing *Wonderwall* to a badly tuned guitar.

Moment 24:
Down Town
by Marek Kohn

This is a moment you can share by walking down North Street towards the Steine and turning left by the bank into Bond Street, preferably on a sunny day.

Bond Street is a place where different visions of Brighton rub along happily. It has the upmarket labels, the high retailers' margins, the air of smartness to gladden the hearts of those whose vision of the city's future revolves around branding and enterprise. At the same time it has the qualities cherished by those who don't want progress to spoil Brighton's peculiar character. It's cheerful, it's colourful, it's homely, and it doesn't look like anywhere else. Chic sits comfortably with quirkiness. The tool shop and the latest fashion boutique complement each other, even though the former has been going strong since 1880 and the latter has been there five minutes.

All this is what you see around you. But a curious thing happens if you look beyond where you're going. Look straight ahead – the effect is best on the left-hand side of the street – and you will see the Downs. It's just a small rectangle of hillside, partly framed by St Bartholomew's Church; it looks almost like a trick of the eye, cut from the country and pasted into the town.

For those of us whose hearts are lifted in summer by the Downland arcs of green hill against sheer blue sky, this little cameo is like a lark's song hovering above the street. More than that, though, it's a reminder that Brighton is not just surrounded by the Downs but is part of them. We think of it as a seaside town, or the dominant half of a city by the sea, but we take for granted the ground beneath our feet. Although it's impossible to be unaware that the streets roll over hills, behind the blinkers of everyday routine this may seem no more than an inconvenience, or if you prefer, an opportunity for exercise.

But hills bring more than toil to everyday life. They bring change, and energy, and visions. Above all, they shape the townscape. Brighton's beauty, taken as a whole, lies not in the age or details of its buildings but in their relationship to the hills they are built on. By a fortunate historical accident, the way the Victorians built happened to harmonise perfectly with the hillsides upon which they transformed Brighton from a fishing village with Regency pretensions into the kernel of a city. The terraces and the railway station's canopies follow the contours of the Downs; the viaduct adds its own expansive curve, joining the two great hills of east and west Brighton across the valley where a river should run, but never has. Brighton is urban downland, contours and curves, human and intimate but with moments of glory.

Nature provides many of those moments, sometimes many in the course of a single day. I can look out of my window on the western hill and see a storm approaching over the eastern slope. Sometimes I can't see the eastern slope at all, for the sea-mist. 'Fog on the Level: Hanover Isolated.' Nature rebuts the cliché about Brighton being 'London by the sea'. In London you can't see the weather coming, nor the land on which the city is built. You never really know where you are.

Here in Brighton, not only do the Downs let us know where we are, but they also provide us with changes of perspective, corners turned and clouds passing, new sights and ways of seeing, like the wooded hillside at the far, far end of Bond Street. They open moments for that characteristically Brighton activity: gazing into the distance.

Moment 25:
Home Thoughts from Abroad
by Martine McDonagh

1. On the corner of 3rd and Pine, downtown Seattle, stands a man. A bus passes him, then another and another, in quick succession. He waves them on, stretching out his right arm beyond the edge of the sidewalk so that his fingertips graze the side of each bus as he hurries it on to its mid-block stop ahead. Bus number three gets a special smile and salute and a shout made unintelligible by alcohol.

He is more unkempt than his dapper Brighton counterpart, his hair dirtier, less recently trimmed. He is younger, probably never even reached retirement age in the job that he continues voluntarily. His coat is grubby from standing too long by the roadside, too close to the traffic, or from lounging in doorways on his lunchtime booze-break or in bus shelters when the working day is done and all the drivers have gone home.

2. In the Doug Fir Lounge in Portland, Oregon – it's important to specify that this is not Portland, Maine or Portland, Idaho, or Portland Road, Hove, where such a phenomenon would never occur – punters form an orderly single file, like a queue for cinema tickets, for service from the solitary barman. On a busy Saturday, the line will stretch up the stairs and out of the door into the warm West Coast night.

3. San Francisco, one huge Brighton Moment: the in-your-face, bums-on-streets Brighton of ten years ago and the laptop layabout, ethical entrepreneur-occupied Brighton of 2008. Gays, activists, corporate hedonists: those who live against the prevailing wind. White terraced hills, grey chilly mists and of course the sea. But all on a grander scale (think West Pier, Golden Gate Bridge), as if Brighton were grown from a seed blown on a furious westerly across the Atlantic and dropped on the English south coast. That's how it seems. But we all know the seed blew or flew the other way, against the prevailing wind. Which is perhaps why we have pebbles

and they have sand.

4. The young man seated on the seafront bench, his acoustic guitar propped on a raised and bent knee, stopped me, as I had known he would, and asked would I listen to his song, written the night before. Strumming, staring out at the storm that raged over Deauville or Cherbourg (or maybe it was Malibu or Big Sur. Where was I?), he repeated the song's hook, a simple four-word question, over and over. I forget the specifics, but probably it had something to do with a lover coming back. Or not. But what mattered to the songwriter – I could tell – were not those four words and the question they posed. It was the inspiration of imagined heartbreak and the power of his voice against the crash of the waves that fed him. The song itself was nonsense, delivered by the voice of an angel.

I filled the silence, which followed the last chord, with words as trite as his lyric: beautiful, angel, simple. With a mutual thank you and a handshake we said goodbye.

Moment 26:
Under the Minarets
by Alison MacLeod

The moon is as ripe and heavy as a piece of fruit about to fall. Above us, the domes loom, fat and golden. Minarets conjure Samarkand, Bukhara, St. Petersburg. Beyond the lawns, the Number Two to Rottingdean chugs past.

'This is good,' Bahrom decides, nodding like a connoisseur. 'But in Moscow, we have better.'

I smile. 'It's not Red Square.'

'Still, I like. Is beautiful.'

'A prince lived here.'

'Ah.' He tries to stare more respectfully.

'But it was always more make-believe than real.'

He assembles the words in his mouth. 'More *make belief.*'

Clouds scud past, their bellies floodlit. I don't know how to explain: about Kubla Kahn, pleasure domes, and the nineteenth-century whim for all things Eastern. How do I say that the Pavilion is a pun on the onion-domes and turrets he has known all his life?

He stretches out on the grass, making himself into a bed for me, making even his upturned hands into resting places for my arms. How good he is to kiss. How solid he is below me. After nine months of grieving, I have been pulled back into the world.

His voice is deep and mild. He tells me the story of a relative, an old bear of a man who bites the faces of his favourites at family weddings, bruising them, drawing blood sometimes, but unstoppable. He demonstrates, getting hold of my cheek between his grin until I wrestle my face away. His teeth are white and strong. He opens wide and points inside – the backs are lacquered black. I thought only old men chewed tobacco.

When he tells me he was born in Tajikistan, not Russia, I ransack my brain. Do I even know it? Have I somehow overlooked an entire country? 'Samarkand is once ours,' he continues. 'My grandfather is birthed in Samarkand.'

I can think only of spices, Tamburlaine and ululating women. It is less real to me than *The Arabian Nights*.

'But Stalin gives Samarkand as gift to Uzbekistan. He change our borders to make it theirs.' He studies my hand, then kisses it. 'You have very sugary toes.'

'Very sweet fingers?'

'Yes,' he nods, impatient – I am a pedant. He hums a few bars from the new single by Lemar, 'If There's Any Justice'. Then, 'Do you know, in just one day, Stalin orders 300,000 imams killed. My grandfather loses all his fingers fighting.'

'But he lived?'

'Yes, he is re-settled by Stalin to Duschanbe, the capital. Is very nice. Boulevards. Trees with many leafs. Good restaurants. University. Mountains which hug the city. But we are no longer Persian. No longer Muslim. Only Soviet. Pure Soviet. Then civil war comes when I am thirteen. My teacher shouts, run, run. I fall off the bus and break both my...?' He shows me.

'Wrists.'

'They bomb houses on my street. If a man is birthed in wrong part of country, they pull him from his home, from his bedroom at night, and shoot. I go with my father and other men. In darkness, we bury our neighbours in park at end of street. There is one I see in my sleep for long time. Two bullets in his chest. One in his head. His body burnt. They say he works for secret newspaper. I remember him most of all because they cut off his nose and ears.'

I run my fingers over the stubble of his cropped black hair. 'And your father?'

'My father is for Islamic Democratic Party. Not good. We must leave. There is another milk factory for him to manage. In Moscow. We even have chauffeured car. We are lucky, *inshallah*.'

As a boy, he carried an oxygen mask in his backpack. At school, he was evacuated once a week in preparation for a nuclear attack by the Americans. If a neighbour visited the West, the KGB descended upon the street. They knocked on doors: 'What has he told you about his visit? What does he boast?'

These days, Bahrom is proud of Putin's might. He misses the Soviet passport, its authority in the world. 'No vun knows Tajikistan.'

In my bedroom in the mornings, he races through a routine of one-armed press-ups. He stands and twists quickly at the waist, popping the air between his joints. He grabs the door lintel, the top of the frame, and hauls himself up and down, up and down. In his jersey boxers, with his light skin and wide cheekbones, he looks like a 1950s Soviet athlete.

Who would dream that his mother and father had the same great, great, great grandfather; that this great-great-great had four wives; that he worshipped fire as a way to God? 'But after Stalin,' Bahrom explains, 'every science book at school begin with same sentence: "There is no God."' His mother is a physics teacher. In their Moscow apartment, his family celebrates holy days with the curtains drawn.

On the Pavilion lawn, his phone vibrates between our hips. He reaches for his pocket. 'Hello Moto,' he sings to his phone, a new purchase from Churchill Square. He flips it open – '*Da*' – and slips into a blend of Russian and Persian. I roll off so he can speak. He stands and walks, phone to ear. His brow creases. He thrusts his free hand deep into a pocket. He shouts briefly, then ends the call.

At a bush, he snaps off the stalk of a heavy-headed hydrangea and returns with it for me. I smile, my nose among its purple petals. 'You're not allowed to pick the flowers.'

'Always an odd number,' he says. 'One, three, five. An even number of flowers is bad luck.' He opens my bag and settles it inside.

'What was it? On the phone.'

He shrugs. 'Nothingk.' And as if to prove it, he turns a cartwheel in the grass. He tumbles upside-down and walks on his hands in the shadows of the Pavilion's scaffolding.

We walk past Grand Parade and toward the London Road. The Pavilion's minarets recede behind us. We pass the old Bingo hall, and he snaps a picture of the eye-sore of a sign with his mobile. We pass Sainsbury's, McDonald's, my dry-cleaner's. He speaks to me in Persian, and I laugh. Suddenly he is a stranger to me.

'In Persian, I tell you how happy I am beside you. I tell you in Persian because it is best language for emotions. Like poetry. Pictures. Many pictures. Uzbek too. Turkish is quite good. Russian, not very.'

'And English?'

'I learn only slowly.'

No wonder. His language school in Hove has been shut down three times by the police. Each time, the owner, an Egyptian, waits a month, maybe two, then changes the name in the window.

'The Regency School of English'. 'The Imperial School of English Language Studies'. 'The Sussex College for English Language Proficiency'. Mr Hafez rents accommodation to his students. Cheap but still over-priced. Bahrom sleeps in a room with four other men. 'Is okay,' he says. 'Like brothers.' Recently, he brought home a fifth. An Uzbek. 'What could I do? He sleep on potato sacks on kitchen floor in London restaurant. I give him my bed till Turkish student leaves, and I get him job vashing dishes.'

At the Italian restaurant in the Lanes, everyone in the kitchen is either Asian or middle eastern. Few are legal. As a line-cook, Bahrom makes deep-dish lasagne and steamed mussels in a creamy white wine sauce. He has respect for food, for the pleasures of the senses. He is good. But in the basement, far below the feet of the clientele, tempers flare each night in the heat and steam.

Soon, the new salad-man – surly, unpredictable, a stranger to everyone – will up-end a kettle of bubbling tomato sauce and run. Bahrom will be rushed up the stairs and through the back door out of view of the diners. At the hospital they will discover second- and third-degree burns. Doctors will encourage him to press charges. But the salad-maker will not be found, and the owner will visit Bahrom in hospital and give him £50 for his troubles. Bahrom wants to keep working. He must have money to show for himself when he returns to Moscow in November. Already his father boasts, 'My son, big chef in good restaurant in London.'

London. Brighton. It's all relative.

In my fridge sits our supper: mushroom tagliatelle in a sauce he has made from scratch. But at my door, he kisses me and tells me to eat well.

'What do you mean? Where are you going?'

'A problem.'

'The phone call.'

'I'm sorry.'

'Stay.'

'Do not vorry.'

'When you say that I worry.'

'I see you at parade tomorrow. Do not forget to put our flower in vahter.'

A Cadillac glides past St. Peter's. Two hairy-armed dames perch on the back seat, blowing kisses to the crowd. The song from an open-topped bus explodes behind them. 'So horny, horny, I'm horny, horny, horny...' Balloon-bouquets and boas rise into the air. Men in Marie Antoinette wigs totter on stilts toward the crowd, their tanned buttocks quivering. A Japanese princess-boy waves from beneath her tall golden headpiece. Across the London Road, a party spills onto a narrow roof. Bubbles stream from their open window. A blonde in a tasselled leather waistcoat and mini cowgirl skirt slaps her thighs and fires twin pistols at the sun. Her friend twirls a lasso and chugs champagne as the Gay Police Association marches respectably past.

A kiss on my ear. I turn and Bahrom circles my shoulders with his arms.

'See? Like I promise. I find you.'

I lay my hands over his, then lift them, staring. His knuckles are bruised and bloody.

He points, as if I'm a child who might be distracted. 'Look! My God!' Men in Vegas-style feather costumes can-can past. The crowd is a froth of cheers and whistles. He reaches for his phone and switches on the camera.

I grab the phone. His eyes meet mine. We escape the press of bodies and walk to a patch of St. Peter's dried-out lawn.

'Yesterday, a guy from the school, a Tajik guy, I don't know him much, he sees a girl from Kazakhstan he likes at station. He asks for her number. She is stupid. She gives it.'

'Why stupid?'

'Because she has boyfriend, a Kazakh, who hears about it. Then a car with his friends find Tajik guy. He says he doesn't know about a boyfriend. But is no good. I get that call. We all must go.'

'Where?'

Bahrom rips grass from the ground. 'An empty petrol station on the seafront.'

The Tajiks versus the Kazakhs, like a scene-gone-wrong from *West Side Story*. Where am I?

'Is terrible. The Kazakh, he hit and hit, and the Tajik guy, he not so big. Finally, I feel so ill in my stomach I go and pull the Kazakh off him. His friends, they shout and get big with it and they say I am against the rules – yes, but I can't let it happen more – so they come on me and we all fight. Is bad for everyone. Two of us, we get the Tajik to the hospital – a broken rib and this and that. It takes a long time in 999. Then home, sleep two hours, shower – and find you. I promise, yes, and I find you.'

I lay my hand on his. It's trembling.

He looks up, shaking off the night. 'How is flower?'

'Perfect.'

'My English not good today.'

'You're tired.'

He laughs, falling back to rest his head on the ground. 'My brain gets bad. Before I learn languages easy. My father tell me now I learn enough. He has business ready for me.'

'Where?'

'In Nowhere.'

'Close to Moscow?'

'No. Far.'

'Will you need English for the business?'

'No. I vill forget.' He winces in the sunshine, looks at me, then away again. 'I fear I vill.'

November. I stare at the map on my screen. I try to imagine him in the black dot that is labelled 'Ufa'. He stands outside an internet café in temperatures of fifteen below. 'Brighton', he is saying, but the signal is bad. 'It feel like you, Brighton, your flat, Churchill Square, all the flowers, like' He sighs. 'Is no good. Already, I don't know the vords.'

'*Try*,' I say down the phone. 'Try to remember.'

'Here is jungle. You cannot imagine. For example, my eyes are wet a little now, yes?, because I speak with you, and people by door they look like they vish to kill me for it. You, Brighton, speaking English, Pavilion – remember? – is all like... like... I don't know.'

'Bahrom, sweetheart, listen, isn't there anyone you know?'

'Is all like... the vord you teach me for Pavilion.'

My heart is a stone in my chest. 'Make-believe?' For a moment, dead air. 'Bahrom...?' I see again his huge black eyes, the rise of his chest, the archipelago of burn-marks on his back. Outside my window, a girl with fly-away pink hair walks past.

Then his voice again, deep but faint, reaching across 2,300 miles. 'Yes. Make belief. You understand? Listen to me. That is vord. I *make belief*.'

<u>Moments 27-33:</u>

<u>Moment 27:</u>
Come and See Invisible Ice
Cream Van in Brighton
by Asako Masunouchi

Come & See
Invisible
Ice Cream Van
in Brighton

<u>**Moment 28:**</u>
Brighton Route #1
by Roderick Mills

LONDON
VICTORIA

CLAPHAM JUNCTION

EAST CROYDON

REDHILL

Horley

GATWICK AIRPORT

THREE BRIDGES

Balcombe

HAYWARDS HEATH

Wivelsfield

Burgess Hill

Hassocks

Preston Park

BRIGHTON

Moment 29:
Sunrise
by Dan Mumford

<u>**Moment 30:**</u>
Burnt Offerings
by Gary Powell

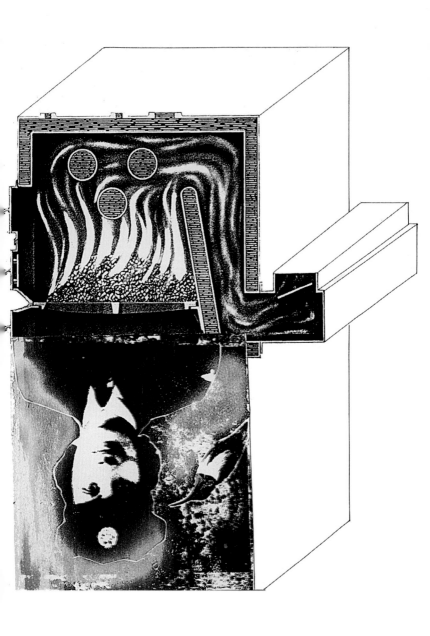

<u>Moment 31:</u>
Discovering Snooper's
Paradise
by Corinna Radcliffe

<u>Moment 32:</u>
Royal Pavilion Seagull
Airport
by Natsko Seki

Royal Pavilion

Seagull Airport

<u>Moment 33:</u>
Summer Seafront Bike Ride to
Hove Lagoon at Sunset
by Alice Stevenson

Moment 34:
Jazz Hands
by Tanya Murray

Summer, 2006. A Friday, late afternoon. And the annual camping trip of the Brighton Transsexual and Bisexual Swimming Club was off to a rocky start.

'I'm sorry sir, you simply can't pitch your tent there. It's right in the middle of the site access road.'

'Sir? *Sir*? What are these, then, sunshine, bloody burger baps?'

Debs, outraged, took each of her not inconsiderable tits in a meaty fist and squeezed them in the direction of the flustered-looking retired-officer type before her. Officer-type winced. His right hand clenched reflexively for a swagger stick that hadn't been there for at least a decade. He settled instead for a clearing of his throat, a tensing of his shoulders, a jutting of his jaw. Silence descended. A stand-off.

Behind Debs, her tent – a relic of the heavy canvas and steel pole variety last seen gracing scout camps in the 1960s – leaned creaking into the stiffening breeze, suspended in a state of precarious semi-construction.

We'd arrived on site all of ten minutes before but Debs, as usual, was already making her presence felt. Her stiletto heels, high-gloss stockings, tight pencil skirt and silk blouse adorned with a delicate string of pearls gained a certain *je ne sais quoi* in contrast with the muddy Weymouth field. It wasn't quite the outfit most people would choose to go camping in, but then, Debs wasn't most people.

'It's madam, mate, and don't you forget it,' she grated.

She usually worked on building sites where, I imagined, her deep, penetrating and unabashedly male voice would cut across the din of cement mixers, pneumatic drills and the protests of people she disagreed with. Debs often did disagree with people. Sometimes physically.

Officer-type, owner of this campsite, the only site in Weymouth we'd been able to find plots on this busy weekend – the one place therefore that we really, really needed to stay if this whole trip

103

wasn't to descend into fiasco before it even started – hesitated.

I imagined his previous career: facing down terrorists in Northern Ireland perhaps; negotiating with trigger-happy tribal chiefs in Afghanistan; hunting war criminals in Kosovo. Nothing had prepared him for this.

He swept his gaze across our random convoy. Five vehicles, fifteen people. Not, it was fair to say, your usual happy campers. His gaze had in it just a hint of fear.

A bisexual white couple, man and woman, caught his eye first. Both sported Dayglo, dreadlocked hair in several clashing shades, each wearing enormous, shapeless fun-fur coats in electric shades of blue and pink. They had driven down in an old VW minibus. The fur coats, the graphic, punky makeup both wore gave them the look of cuddly toys designed by a psychopath. Surrounded by nice, neat Halfords-bought family tents, they were as exotic and threatening as vultures in a suburban garden.

The enormous tent they were constructing echoed their style: a maximalist creation, swathed in heavy scarlet velvet drapes and zebra-striped rugs, huge cushions and bean bags. It oozed louche-ness and debauchery, a flat-packed canvas whorehouse. Heavy incense drifted into the air from two burners at the entrance. This lurid creation was already attracting quizzical, faintly worried glances from our temporary new neighbours.

Just then, a muffled thud came from inside their vehicle and it occurred to me it was just as well that Officer-type, and all the brightly smiling families with their 2.4 kids encamped about us, didn't know about the *other* essential accessory the couple had brought down with them. Their rubber slave. The gimp they planned on keeping locked in their van the whole time they were here, untying him once in a while only for a little light torture, psychological abuse, or closely observed use of toilet facilities. Not necessarily in a toilet.

The rest of us ranged in outrageousness and fashion sense from gender queer, through obvious bull dyke and camp queen, to, frankly, confused. Typified by Paul aka Paula, who would be one or the other depending on her/his mood. A close study of the acces-sorising he/she had done on any given occasion was usually the key to guessing correctly, I had discovered. And yes, the whole people in glass houses thing was evident to me in every one of my exchanges with her. But still... All I could say in defence of my own gender confusion was that it was at least consistent. Girl in a boy's body, blah blah blah. God, how bored was I with that script by now?

Queenly shrieks rang out from another of our encampments-under-construction, but most of our multi-gendered crew had left off their preparations to form a loose circle around Officer-type and Debs, keen to see how this showdown would pan out. It seemed highly likely that it would end with us leaving the site. Maybe – I didn't entirely discount the possibility – in police vans.

I felt a pang of sympathy for Officer-type. Our fashion sense as confused as our gender profiles, it ran the gamut from rubber through bondage to drag and back again, via a smattering of muddy combats and DM boots. On the scale of camping normality, only the boots and combats were okay. Though on the plus side, sort of, plenty of *technically* waterproof clothing was in evidence. Only not much of it was from Millets.

Officer-type finished his survey. He swallowed, drawing on centuries of British stiff upper lip. Rorkes Drift, Goose Green, Basra... And now: Weymouth. When he spoke, his voice was calm. Only the minutest twitch of live flesh at the corner of his eye betrayed him.

'Well –'

He hesitated. Debs's toil-roughened hands, tipped in dagger-like scarlet ceramic nail extensions, bunched and flexed. The threat of violence hung in the air. I edged closer, ready to step in. Just in case.

Officer-type forced a tight, polite smile.

'Um... *madam*,' he began.

Debs's fists unclenched, just a little.

'Perhaps the misunderstanding was my fault. I did say you could pitch anywhere, did I not? Only... not here. Just...' Another quick swallow, another nervous glance around our group. 'Not here, that's all. Cars, access, you know... So could I ask you instead, uh, madam,' it came easier the second time, 'just to move your tent back, just a few feet? Please? Madam?'

The third *madam* was the charm. Mollified, Debs grunted agreement. A collective sigh of relief ran round our circle. This year's Transsexual & Bisexual Swimming Club of Brighton Annual Camping Trip was, at last, in full effect.

Officer-type staged a gracious retreat.

As he left, he paused by our subset of the group, perhaps because in my nondescript combats he took me for the man I had once been, and Lisa for the natural born woman she always was. In the context of the rest of our little set, I suppose we looked almost normal.

He nodded, smiled reflexively, took one last look around at this motley-garbed crew which had descended, like invaders from space, onto his nice country campsite.

'So, er –' He hesitated. Trying to understand it all. To understand *us*. There had to be a reason, for all this sudden – weirdness. And then, his brow unfurrowed. Of course. In a second, it all made perfect sense. At last, he *got* it.

'I take it you lot must be with the, uh... jazz festival?'

I smiled politely. I seriously doubted if there was one amongst us who could play so much as *Greensleeves* on a recorder.

Moment 35:
Now is the Time
by Jeff Noon

Picture if you will some old public house down some halfway forgotten side street. One of those places where the light is always painful and sharp, so that every last punter is lit up brightly in all their glory. Picture them. There they are, mapped in lines of cigarette drift. They breathe and drink and cough and spit and drink some more, filling the air around themselves with cries and mumblings, howls of pain, sudden piercing declarations of undying love. This is the place.

Now see. You're standing just inside the doorway, hardly daring to move. Some kid from the sticks, just needing some kicks, some fuse to be licked, that's you. Too young, too shy, too fearful. Eyes downcast, avoiding the stares, sick and tired of being laughed at, jeered at. Well here it is. Upon this damp and sticky evening you could maybe take a step or two. Keep moving, keep going, one step, another, one more. Hold your skin tight, close your pores. Gird your striped mohair jacket around yourself proud. Now let them stare. Keep your scarlet-coloured trousers hitched up high to show off your ankles, wrapped as they are in their apple-green socks. And wearing your hair long in the fringe, combed back on the top. Looking good, feeling good. The night begins.

Brighton, 1962.

From where does it arise, this strange desire to make an exhibition of yourself, to be your very own work of art? To be shouted at, sneered at, by your father, your teachers, and all the bosses of the world. To be beaten for your efforts. Even by your former friends, beaten. And you don't know why, or where the impulse comes from that makes you adorn yourself thus, except that you must, you can do no other thing.

You've travelled along some rumours to find yourself here, walking through the bar, past the hand-written poster pinned to the wall. These words: TONIGHT! FROM LONDON, BEAT GROUP SENSATION – THE NOW! Up a short flight of stairs, where some greasy article takes your money and then you're through. Into a pokey back room, half-empty, the people all standing around, most of them young like yourself. And you note with surprise the few dots of colour here and there in a black and white world, like your own colours, like semaphore. Here you wait, not daring to speak to anyone. Here. Waiting. Now. Watching as the group walk on stage, plug in. Howls of feedback and then music, and then words sung out fiercely. And no matter that the band are almost breaking this song apart, so loud they're playing it and with such a shabby charm, it's the exact shabbiness and the loudness that's bringing the shakes upon you. It feels like they're sending the words and the beat out directly towards you, you alone.

You. Alone.

Closer, come closer now. Feeling the stir, the moment, some small bud within your breast, cracking open. Here it is, the force that drives you accelerating forwards, to the stage. The four young men moving there. Guitar strings, silver flash, drum skin, bass boom, BOOM! Make room, and then zoom yourself, zoom close. The singer, there he is, with his long and his lean, with his eyes set to wild and his hair all jet-black and spruced-up on top, draped in front, like your own. And his mouth working like a broken machine: Why don't you, baby, take an x-ray of the city, take a blade to the moon and taste the slice of it, baby, illuminate your tongue with the moon's glow. Yeah, something like that. Words, a blur of words. This is your time, my baby, can't you hear me?

Closer. Reaching out. The noise and the colour and the speed all inside you, and the sheer electrical love of it all, the dazzle of it, the spark and the heat of it, exploding all around you. The sheer hard, soft, cold, fiery love of it all. Like somebody just turned the night on, clicked a hidden switch. Release. Illuminated. Electrified! Closer, touching. Until the song has a hold on you completely and it's then that you know: your whole stupid fucking crazy mixed up life suddenly clicking into shape, turning, burning, and then realising now at last that no longer, no longer were you alone in the world. Because this is the place. This place, your place. This night, your night.

To be folded here, safely, lost and found in the space between.

And then out, down to the sea.

Enough for now, this will do it. Trying to keep the feelings tight inside you, never wanting to lose them. It's like the rain falling soft with its blessing. It's like that moment of the day when the lights first come on along the promenade, the rain falling harder now and the lights making their glow in the downpour, and maybe a loud desperate cry from a doorway, or else a boy and a girl shivering on a bench, clinging together like the only warm place for miles around is where their lips meet, the breath, the mingled caressing of breath. And then the sky torn apart by forked lightning far out over the sea, out where the world curves away, drops away, the darkness lit by the lightning and then dark once more, darker than before, the water curving away out of sight and leaving you all alone here, gathered here, yourself and all the lost souls like you, soaked to the bones here, now. You're just making your dreams happen as you can from the few ragged scraps of small-town life that now and again come floating by on the wind, the rain, the cold white moon.

This is your time, my baby. Can't you hear me?

Echoes. Listen.

This is your time now, baby, can't you hear me?

This is your time, my baby.

Listen.

This is your time now, baby,

Can't you hear me...

Moment 36:
Complete with Gull
by Jed Novick

I love the gulls. I love the way they look in the night sky. I love the way they don't care. I love the noise they make. I love the way they just do what they want. What I like most about the gulls is they don't care what we think. They don't do that cute *Oooh tickle my tummy* cuddly animal thing. They don't care. They don't care about anything except gulls.

I'm going to sit here and do nothing. I'm going to shout and make as much noise as I want. There's a bin liner. I'm going to rip that bag open. See what's in it. Make a mess. Look, a car coming out of the carwash. Good. I needed a poo. I can do anything I like and no one can stop me.

Gulls are beautiful. They're smart. They're perfectly designed. And they're sexy. You know those posh sports cars with doors that lift up from the roof? What are they called? Gullwing. Not hawk-wing or eaglewing or piedwagtailwing. Gullwing.

I love the gulls. They're masters of the universe.

A couple of years ago I was talking to the bloke next door. Generally, he's a top man, a good neighbour. Goes on holiday a lot. Anyway, he had one of those *pleased with myself* looks. I asked him what he was looking pleased about.

'We had a seagull nest on the roof. Bloody things, but I've got them. I got this piece of wood, about a metre square, and banged a load of nails through it. Then I went up and carefully put it under the seagull nest. You can't have bloody seagulls nesting on the roof. The noise, the mess...'

So anyway, I went up to my attic and had a look out at the neighbour's house. And smiled. There on his roof – and this is a true story, I swear – was this piece of wood with nails sticking through it. And next to it was a carefully constructed seagull nest, complete with gull.

Anyway, the reason I'm talking about this is, to paraphrase Mrs Thatcher, we're going to be a godfather. I work in the attic of our house. I did have an office in town – it was in Jew Street and

I couldn't resist – but there are so many problems with that idea. You've got to get up, get dressed, and go there. And this isn't just once or twice. This is every day I'm talking here. Believe me, working at home is much, much easier. All that essential stuff that freelance writers have got to do – watering the plants, making sure all the cutlery is in the right place, checking that you watered all of the plants – you can't do that in an office.

So one day I'm sitting there, writing, well, thinking, planning what I'm going to write, and I hear a bit of squawking. OK, so hearing a gull squawk isn't exactly *hold-the-front-page* stuff but this was, I don't know, a different kind of squawking. Reluctantly, I dragged myself away from my keyboard and looked out of the window.

And there she was. Sitting on a perfectly made pile of twigs and leaves like a queen on a throne. The proudest look on her face. Kvelling like only a mother can kvell. Just above her, on the chimney stack, was the old man. Chest puffed out, and on the lookout. Keeping it safe. Trying to look important and ready for action. He saw me and we looked at each other. I held his gaze and we nodded. An understanding. (Listen, I know we're deep in men's group stuff – Iron John stuff – here, but bear with me). I've been through this. I know what he's thinking and I know what she's thinking.

He's thinking: *I'm going to be a dad. I can do anything. I'm going to rip some bin liners open. I can do anything I like.*

She's thinking: *God knows how that happened with that idiot who spends his life with his head in a rubbish bag. Still, if he gets me some food, I'll be nice to him.*

I went downstairs and got some bread. Immediately Jane was onto me.

'I thought you were going wheat free? Really, what is the point of... You're giving it to a seagull?'

It was OK. She understood.

He's almost tame now, the old man. Comes to the window and sits. Picks up my bits of food and checks his sudoku grids. Mostly though he sits there on the chimney stack making seagull noises and trying to look useful.

We've moved on from bread; apparently she's on some no-carbs diet. And I'm throwing out all different stuff now. I know what gulls eat because I know what they leave behind when they rip open the bin liners and basically, you know, they don't leave anything behind. Jane said – and very funny, this – 'When the babies are born

maybe you should make some tiny black bin liners for them to prac-
tise on.'

She still hasn't moved. Every so often she gives the old man a
hard time and he does that useless bloke shrug we all do. I look at
them. They look at me. I can't wait. It's going to be a good summer.

<u>Moment 37:</u>
Brief Encounter in
Bill's Café
by Sally O'Reilly

There's never any space here. The wooden benches are crowded with fat toddlers, relentless uber-mums and scary Brighton dads with professional papooses. Behind them, banks of cinematic fruit, waxy lemons, Technicolor strawberries. Daily menus, indulgently wholesome, chalked up on little black boards. Charred veg with everything.

Why did I bring the baby here? Just bloody-minded, that's my problem. Jackson is already screwing his face up into a Les Dawson gurn, ready to start screeching for a feed. Should have gone to Starbucks. I mean, look at them in their Camper boots and retro-horn rims. Barging into each other, then apologising with attitude. What is it with these women? Some kind of Boudicca complex? They act like those three-wheeled buggies come with blades attached.

And why do they think breast feeding is an extreme sport? A little modesty wouldn't go amiss. I tried a bit of stylish suckling myself, once, at a country wedding. Accidentally ended up topless in the family photos. Wrong kind of dress. Bruised by this experience, I seek out dark corners so I can shove Jackson up my jumper for a furtive slurp. Even then, I'm a magnet for the criminally insane.

Finally, a seat. One empty chair, opposite a member of the Maternal Majority, breast feeding, naturally, bare naked whammer the size of a football. Cup of herbal in front of her. She's wearing a cloche hat enlivened with knitted fruit.

'Is any one sitting here?'

She shakes her head. 'Help yourself.'

I collapse in front of her and attach Jackson to my right breast. Her baby is glugging like a lager lout. We exchange a look, not con-spiratorial, exactly. But not hostile.

'How old is yours?' she asks after a while.

'Ten weeks.'

'Boy or girl?'

'Boy. Jackson.'

She says nothing, as if letting this sink in. Jackson. My mother wanted me to call him Sebastian. Boyfriend was all for Wolf. But, as he'd left me, his views weren't very influential.

'Mine's a girl,' she says.

'Oh.'

'Nearly four months.'

'Lovely.'

'Rafaella.'

'Right.'

We drink our tea in silence. Divided by a common experience. Before I had a baby, I dreaded turning into a mum. And now it turns out I was right. They're the worst people I've ever met. After a bit, she unlatches the baby and winds it on her shoulder, on one of those NCT muslin shawls that you have to keep in a Cath Kidston changing bag. Then she looks at me. She has violet eyes, clear and shining with a stab of laughter behind them.

'Never thought I'd see the day. Did *you*?'

'Which day?'

'You know. This...' Her laugh is like a question mark. 'All this baby bollocks. I was a proper person once.'

She has three spots on her pointed chin, dark rings under her starry eyes. She's beautiful.

Slurp of tea. I watch her over the rim of my cup. She takes her stupid hat off. She has cropped yellow hair. Then, I blink madly. The café is wavering with tears. Something's flown into my eye.

She leans forward. 'Stay still.'

'It's okay, it's nothing...' I rub my hot eye, my wet cheek.

Placing Rafaella across her knee, she takes the muslin from her shoulder. 'Don't move. Don't...' She wipes my eye, swift and expert. 'There! Got it! Tiny fly or something.'

'Thank you.' I shake my head, trying to return the world to its familiar shapes. I don't want to catch her eye again. I put my glasses on. They're not modish. They make me look like Anne Widdecombe.

Now she's grinning, filling up all the space in my head.

'Your baby's called "Jackson", but who are you?'

'Alex.'

'I'm Laura.' She touches my hand. 'We should do this again.'

I look down at her freckled fingers, waiting for my next breath to come.

'Old married women, meeting up for tea,' she says. 'That's what passes for excitement now.'

'Sad, isn't it?' I manage at last. 'Like some 1940s throwback.'

'Terribly, terribly dated,' she says, in a Celia Johnson voice.

Jackson has fallen off my breast. A trail of milk drools over the side of his face, and his little alien hands jerk upwards, as if to save himself from falling.

Moment 38:
The Sea End of Wardour Street
by Chris Paling

I was talking to a friend about Brighton and we agreed that cities are not just places they're states of mind. So where is Brighton? I asked him.

I thought he'd know. He's a well-educated man, in fact he used to work in the bookshop where John Lennon met Yoko Ono. Once he told me that he remembered her trying to climb into his Mini as he drove away from the shop. It wasn't long before she climbed into his life. Anyway, he knew the Beatles and he knew Jack Kerouac and Ginsberg and Gregory Corso and Frank Zappa. His name is Miles. His Christian name is Barry but everybody calls him Miles. He said that they used to say that Brighton was the sea end of Wardour Street. So that was a place to start: head towards Oxford Street and keep going.

I got here in 1975 and, when I walked out of the station, I knew this was a place I could stay, and maybe belong. But belonging is difficult. Writers find it hard to belong anywhere, whatever they pretend.

Turning down Trafalgar Street I called in at the Nelson and there I met Julie for a drink and I remembered that, when our first child was born, the landlady said we could bring her to the pub and leave her upstairs while we drank in the bar. So we did, but when we got up there the room was full of Victorian china dolls, hundreds of them, standing around watching, sitting on every shelf, evil glass eyes glinting. So we didn't leave our daughter there. The dolls and that landlady are long gone.

We lived in the North Laines and we got to know Pete who painted a Union Jack on his door, and Ted and Joan, and Ted told us that they were going to tear the cottages down in the early sixties and build a flyover so the traffic could get all the way to the seafront without being stuck in jams. But the locals took against the plan and protested and somehow they saved their streets. They also managed to save the old theatre opposite Dockerills but the developer came in one night with his bulldozer and flattened it anyway. For nearly forty years, until they built the new library, the area looked like a bomb site. But, when you live here for a while, you get used to people stealing parts of the town.

They stole the football stadium and built a parade of shops and a new traffic jam.

They imprisoned the sea and called it a marina, and when they did it the developers made a pledge to the people of the town that you would always be able to see the sea from the undercliff walk. But then they stole the sea too and built a supermarket on it, and then a car park, and now they're talking about building skyscrapers on it so soon you won't be able to see the sea at all, just this new traffic jam they've built where the sea used to be.

They stole the West Pier. Actually, before that, they stole the Palace Pier. You must know the story. They took down the old theatre and bar where Pinkie met May and they put it into storage, promising to rebuild it once they'd restored the Palace Pier. But somehow they lost it. A whole theatre, just lost. Occasionally you'd see bits of it around the town, adorning an old building where they sold Christmas trees, bits of panelling in antique shops. But it all went and instead they built a nice plastic barn full of one-armed bandits and put up a huge neon sign advertising the gas the Nazis used in the death camps: Zyclon. There were protests. They took the sign down. Later the West Pier was torched by people in a speed boat, and there was absolutely no suggestion at all, ever, that anybody from the Palace Pier had anything to do with destroying the oldest pier in the country.

Moments.

I remember one night most of all. 1981, I think it was. There was a storm, it was late at night and I went to the beach with Julie. The sea was high. There was nobody around, and we walked onto the pebbles, and a red balloon came bouncing along from the east, from Rottingdean, and bounced away towards Shoreham. And we just watched it go.

In 1975, I set off on a walk through Brighton. It took thirty years and I'm still walking. On the way I learned that belonging is hard, but if they steal your city and it makes you angry, then maybe that's a place to begin.

Moment 39:
The Dipping Jar
by Sue Roe

When I think of Brighton, I don't really think of a moment, I think of what I see – I just dip in and out of the memory for images. In the first road I lived in here, there were palm trees. It seemed like a place quite close to the South of France, with its pinkish light and balmy climate: colourful and maritime. There were red and pink flowers in the gardens of the row of terraced houses spilling down the hill, and at the top of the road a view of other houses stretched against the sky behind the station, which feels like something from another decade, quite archaic. The stations here are oddly rural, you pace up and down waiting for your train in the middle of the countryside, with a view of cabbages and weeds. If you want to buy a ticket you have to toil up some broken steps to the platform for trains going in the opposite direction. Then you stumble down the steps and up another set, to wait for the train that goes where you do want to go. It's like something out of *The Railway Children*. When the train finally comes in, you see a yellow light and a number 36, which is startling because you're expecting steam, great clanking and rattling noises and the unloading of battered leather trunks, not just the odd student with a rucksack and a handful of pasty-faced commuters. I first came here in 1978. Thirty years – have I really been here thirty years? I often meet people who say, 'How long have you lived in Brighton?' and I say, 'Since 1978.' '*1978*? Why haven't I met you before?'

I was looking at the paintings propped up against chair legs in the street outside one of the shops in the Lanes one morning, when the guy came out, a burly guy, like Harold Steptoe, and started on his pitch. 'You like sheep? I got plenty of sheep in the back, you like fields, sky? I got plenty more fields and sky. It's Constable, that one... well, school-of. Come in and have a look. I got cows...' I've had pearl rings with loose pearls, gold earrings that aren't really gold... real Brighton treasures. I once took my Grandmother's ring

Moments 40-46:

Moment 40:
The Calming Mirrors
of Brighton
by Jim Stoten

Moment 41:
Throwing Pebbles
by Lucy Vigrass

<u>Moment 42:</u>
Walking Along the Seafront
to the Furthest of my
Favourite Places in Town,
the Sky Suddenly Comes Alive
by Hannah Waldren

<u>Moment 43:</u>
The Lady's not for Burning
by Steve Wilson

<u>Moment 44:</u>
The Sunday Flea Market — Old
to New, Recycling of Objects
and Ideas, Visual Gum and
the Waft of Fried Onions
by Matt Wingfield

Finding a Pair of Trickers
in a Second-Hand Shop
by Ian Wright

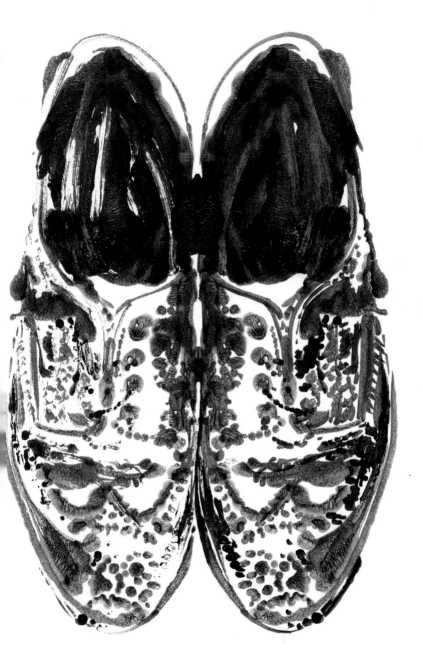

Moment 46:
West St Sat Nite
by Lawrence Zeegen

to a tiny jeweller's in the Lanes, with a window crammed with big old crusty diamonds, asking to have it cleaned. I squeezed my way past hundreds of gold rings (how do they get there? Do so many people die and leave their jewellery to nobody?) and a large, broad-shouldered man with an orange tan, to a little desk with a raddled lady sitting behind it. 'I'll just dip it in here, dear,' she said. At her elbow there was an open jar of liquid. She just picked up my ring in her tweezers, dipped it rapidly in and out, and it came up sparkling. 'What are you doing about the patio area?' she asked her bodyguard with the tan, as if the moment with me and my ring had never actually happened. There's no nonsense, in Brighton, no messing about. They won't shaft you on the important things. No dipping it in the jar, keeping it for a week and charging you a fortune. I suppose she sits there all day, just dipping rings in her jar while he chats to her about the villa in Spain.

The other Lanes, or 'Laines', are a different matter. They're like the other side of the mirror, the dark side, the underbelly. I took a friend from Bristol to the gloomiest, seediest second-hand store and she bought a skirt. I couldn't believe it. From there? All those dead people's clothes, all hung around on crooked wire hangers, still bearing the shapes of their dead owners. I found her a Dior dress, but she didn't want that, just some battered black skirt from the fifties with red flowers on. Yes, it was a good skirt and it suited her but I wasn't sure about the person who'd worn it before, she was still too present in it. I preferred the idea of the wearer of the Dior cocktail dress, whom I could imagine would have had her own cocktail bar at home, and a hostess trolley. But no, my friend wanted the battered black one with the flowers. A man who had been crouched behind a pile of dead women's clothes found her a crumpled carrier bag and took her ten pound note. I suppose he was running the shop.

Then there are the bookshops. There's the remainder bookshop with the gaunt man with interesting bones, faintly decorative and faintly amused, where you can pick up last year's new biographies for a song, and large format books about art, love and death.

There is the serious second-hand bookshop where you find things you've been taking out regularly from the library for years because you're working on the subject, renewing them, taking them back occasionally to show you haven't lost, stolen or sold them on, then taking them out again because you can't find them for sale any-where, on-line or off, before you finally return them to their library home. No sooner have you done that than they'll turn up on the shelves in the serious second-hand bookshop. There's a black cat in that one, and a man who looks as if he's walked out of the 1950s, and jazz playing quietly on a small transistor radio hidden beneath the counter.

You have reincarnation moments in Brighton. I've had several. More than once I have met people for the first time here and been startled by a feeling of primal recognition.

People remind you of your aunt or your grandfather and you know there's a family resemblance, but it may be the big, uncanny family of the reincarnated. Once at a party, standing in someone's garden in the early evening looking over all the little walls, I told a woman I know that the first time I met her, I knew I'd seen her before. She said 'I had exactly the same feeling about you.' The most uncanny of my Brighton moments was one of the earliest. I arrived at a house where I knew there was a room for rent and when the land-lady opened the door I saw her in my writing. In the book I wrote three years later, finished after I left the house, I modelled her on Miss Havisham. A number of years later, she actually died in a fire.

I have had that feeling of recognition a number of times: knowing I go way back with someone. Those moments have always been in Brighton. Maybe Brighton is the name of the Reincarnated People's Home. That would make sense, actually, when you look at some of the faces, some of the characters. The man with the school-of Constable paintings, the lady with the dipping jar, they've obviously been doing those things for centuries.

Twice I've had my fortune told in Brighton. The first time was at the home of Mrs Sonia Sonielli. A friend and I went together, she waited on the sofa and I went first. Mrs. Sonielli and I sat on either side of her dining room table and she said, 'Why am I getting Medieval? I've never had that word before.' Then she told me I was trying to make a decision. She said that if I was trying to decide whether to leave Brighton I should definitely not go. She said, 'You're creative and this is a creative town. This is the right town for you, you can do anything in it, paint pictures, make films... I'm getting wigs.'

When I asked if I could go back for another reading she said no, her arrangement was ten pounds for life membership because on a second reading she wouldn't necessarily see any more. See what

I mean? They don't shaft you here. I went to another fortune teller, who'd come from out of town, who said before we met I should send her something of mine, something that was meaningful to me, not necessarily valuable as such, just an earring or something, which she'd dip in her liquid before the reading so that she wasn't just relying on my astrological chart, it would give her something extra. At first I didn't believe her: she had no dipping jar, she just wanted to make sure I'd turn up. But when she studied her chart even she got Medieval.

I thought I'd have one last try, to see if I got Medieval again. I reckoned the Palace Pier would surely be the best place to get messages from beyond so I made my way past the ice cream stalls, the hot dogs and onions stalls, and out into the briny air, where you can look down and see the sea between the boards, then on past the knock-down-all-the-cans stall, the archery stall, past the big bit of old smelly meat turning round and round in the sea air, and eventually I found a little red, rococo hut, but there was a sign outside: *Space Vacant. Suit Fortune Teller.* Such pragmatism. They don't waste words here.

They don't waste time either, or energy. Everything is conserved. If you put your old table or hairdryer or typewriter out on the street in front of your house, somebody will have found a use for it by tomorrow. Where I live, near the park, the two men with woolly hats come wheeling their pram to the recycling bins, sifting through for old toasters and toys. They inspect things well before selecting their ironmongery, then off they go again between the trees, one wheeling the pram, the other nipping alongside, his eyes still peeled to left and right for new opportunities. Later in the week, the Library Lorry comes lumbering in. I don't think anyone ever borrows books from it here. I think the park is where the driver and her mate come to have their sandwiches. I once heard a rumour that the driver of the Library Lorry was pregnant, but I've never seen the Library Lorry driver's baby up in the cabin.

There are plenty of children's moments, though. You see them all the time, especially in the summer, at the beach, where the reincarnated Victorian children come out to play. The tousled little girl with black laced leather ankle boots and a floral dress, one blisteringly hot August day, standing quietly, apparently unaccompanied, her hot little feet smartly together, eating a leaking ice cream. The tiny girl in a grubby pink net ballet dress twirling round and round on the spot, to the music of the merry-go-round. Two small boys standing hand in hand, one dark, one fair, gazing up at the one-man-band in the Pavilion Gardens, on the morning of the Children's Parade.

Virginia Woolf wrote an essay called *The Moment : Summer's Night*. I have just opened it at random and read, *the moment runs like quicksilver on a sloping board...* which sounds lovely. I imagine a lick of silver light running down the pier, moving in and out between the trees, in the Pavilion Gardens. I don't experience moments like that, though. Mine are more like fireworks, which just flare up and quickly disappear. When I think about moments they present themselves separately, in self-contained images and episodes. I don't think moments run like quicksilver, I think they are more like sparks. Sometimes on a summer's night in Brighton you hear a sudden crack and there are fireworks going off in the sky above the sea, bright, coloured explosions mingling with the lights of the pier and the fabulous, faded grandeur of Brighton, all white plaster and salt, the sky lit up spectacularly in one vivid colour after another, emerald, ruby, pink and yellow diamond dust, making lit, cascading shapes in the air, like a massive kaleidoscope, turning above the waves, falling in pieces down into the dipping jar of the sea then bursting up again, like a fast-motion flowering, into the sky above Brighton.

Moment 47:
Today at the Dentist's
by Nicholas Royle

Today the dentist's. Tist's. Say, *tist's*. My dentist frightens me. Marathon Man meets Wittgenstein. The silent type. *Ent, ist*. He arrived a year or so ago, the latest act at my local NHS pay-as-you-go circus. My dentist is not young. He has big glasses like a snooker player. His hands tremble and he has a speech impediment. *Ment*. Hence perhaps the air of post-Tractatus. He hails from up north. I am convinced he was struck off and has been rehabilitated, incomprehensibly. Hensibly, he *tic*ulates erely *its* of words, when he does peak. Alcohol-illum, Parkinshun, ental break done? I can't help imagining he killed someone. *Man's law. Accidentist.* I have never had any treatment from him, only check-ups, till today. But now two cavities, *tiz*, tizzy, *viz*: both upper right. No mask. He operates as if there is no tomorrow. In goes the injection, like a knife in the street. Blue rubber gloves. I don't know whether to open or shut my eyes. Out of the picture, the indifferent young assistant listens to the radio, looks at her nails. I car peak any more, anaesthetic impacts, in *pax*, hunting in, fingers crossing, tighten, tightest, impacted, *im*-prac-*tist*. And he says nothing, no falsely reassuring *that-should-be-numbing-up-nicely-by-now*, no time for words, he is in like a feeding frenzy in reverse. I keep feeling, as in a dream. Perhaps hallucinatory his halitosis. *Tosis.* Fingers shaking, perspiration beading inside the aquarium spectacles, he lunges, invades, retreats, returns, wielding who knows what, a drill then something else, eels, feels, files, patient eyes closed now for business, long pause as if in exhaustion. Then assault recommences, flailing, thrashing, splay in my mouth, then falls back abruptly with a single word, strangularly tittled out: *done*, he says. He turns as from a scene of a crime and puts down his instruments, like a car mechanic, on the side, still juddering.

Moment 48:
Ancient Bones
by C.J.Sansom

It is December, 1838, and a tall, thin, distinguished-looking man in his late forties stands in an upper room at Number 20, Old Steyne. He is looking across the road to the Royal Pavilion, now closed and empty. His name is Dr. Gideon Mantell, and he has just had to close his fossil museum.

Gideon Mantell was born in Lewes in 1790, the son of a boot-maker. He was a clever lad, and the old woman who kept the infant school he attended grew so attached to him she left him everything in her will. She can't have had much to leave, though, for Gideon was to be short of money all his life. Not that he was ever much interested in money, but he never had enough for what he wanted to do.

He became apprenticed to a local doctor, then 'walked the hospitals' in London as an apprentice before qualifying as a doctor himself. He practised in Lewes, where his reputation was high. At a time when one in thirty mothers died in childbirth, he only lost two out of two thousand births he attended over fifteen years. He was conscientious in his work for the poor, and on one occasion he intervened in a murder case. He wandered by chance into Lewes Crown Court where a woman was on trial for murdering her husband, and by doing a fresh autopsy was able to prove he had died of a heart attack.

Mantell married and started a family. But his great interest was always fossils, the shells and pieces of bone and teeth embedded in stone that were intriguing both professional and amateur scientists and leading some people to question the Book of Genesis which said God created the Earth in six days, six thousand years before. The Geological Debate, one Scottish Minister thundered, *is inconsistent with the testimony of Moses*. But that didn't stop them digging.

When Mantell visited patients in the countryside, he would take his wife Mary, who shared his interests – up to a point – and she would look for fossils round about while he attended to his patients. It was she who found the tooth of a new prehistoric reptile in 1822. Mantell's study of this and other remains led him to conclude that Sussex had once been a tropical forest where herbivorous lizards forty feet long wandered. Nobody then had heard of herbivorous lizards, and even the scientific world thought this was mad. Mantell made contacts with other interested amateurs but found it difficult to break into London and the Royal Society. He was, after all, only a provincial country doctor of common stock, without contacts, and although he was endlessly persistent in his studies when it came to social advancement, Mantell didn't know the meaning of the word 'pushy.'

As the 1820s passed by, Mary Mantell began to get tired of every room in the house being filled with fossils and bits of rock, and lots of dust, and the way her husband would sit up till the small hours chiselling fossilized bones and shells and plants out of lumps of rock. Dr. Mantell didn't listen, though, or not enough. He turned part of his house into a fossil museum. When, in 1830, William IV ascended the throne and visited Lewes, Mantell invited him to see it. He accepted, and they cleaned the house from top to bottom, and the bones too, and put on their best clothes. But he never turned up. It wasn't really William IV's thing. *Pop-eyed and pineapple-headed*, as he was called, he wasn't bright even by the standards of Hanoverian kings. However, he followed his brother George IV in taking up residence in Brighton Pavilion, making the town more fashionable than ever.

The house in Lewes was bursting with fossils now, as well as four children and the surgery, and Mary Mantell was at her wits' end. One of Mantell's correspondents, Lord Egremont, made the suggestion that was to change Mantell's life. Why not sell the Lewes practice, move to Brighton, and set up a new fossil museum near the Pavilion? The lords and ladies would come and visit, he could deliver lectures, perhaps he might even get sponsorship from the Royal Family itself. Lord Egremont suggested it would not be the done thing to charge and, besides, the lords and ladies might not come then, but Mantell could set up a new medical practice in Brighton, with a refined and wealthy clientele. So, in 1833, he sold the Lewes practice and moved to 20 Old Steyne, Brighton.

The museum was a great success. The lords and ladies and courtiers came, though the King didn't. But there was little sponsorship, and, although Mantell's reputation among fossil-hunting scientists was growing in London, and his theories about the plant-eating giant he named *Iguanadon* were becoming accepted, it was agreed in Brighton society that a doctor with a local accent, who spent his spare time among the bones of long-dead monsters, was not the man to deal with their ailments.

And then, in 1837, King William died. The new young Queen, Victoria, disliked Brighton; it was associated with her dissolute Hanoverian uncles and the people were disrespectful; she complained that she could not take a walk along the promenade without rude little errand boys running past her then turning to look up beneath her bonnet to see what her face was like. So the Pavilion closed, and everyone moved away. And so did Mary Mantell; she had had enough of dust and bones and she left her husband, taking their children with her. Mantell was facing bankruptcy. All he could do was sell the house, and his collection. He sold the fossils he had collected over a lifetime to the British Museum. On that evening in December 1838, he wrote in his diary. *What a proof in the vanity of human expectation*. Next morning, ninety carts were needed to remove the collection of a lifetime to London, trundling a long fifty miles through a cold December day. Then Mantell closed the house and followed them, with what money he had, to set up practice in Streatham and continue his studies of the prehistoric world.

Mantell's collection now fell into the hands of a younger scientist, Richard Owen, who in 1841 would coin the name *Dinosauria* to cover the ever-growing number of extinct giants that people were digging up. Owen used Mantell's collection as the basis for much of his research. However, he both belittled Mantell's work and got things wrong. Mantell fought back, and the arguments between them raged throughout the 1840s. Mantell won on points, and achieved a lifetime's ambition when he was awarded a Royal Society medal in 1849.

By that time, though, he was very ill. He was injured in a coach accident not long after leaving Brighton, and thereafter was never free of back problems and in constant pain. He died in 1851, aged sixty-one. At the autopsy they found his lower spine had twisted itself round almost at right angles, something so unusual that it was removed, put in a jar and exhibited at the Hunterian Museum in London, where it still is. So the great student of strange bones himself became an exhibit.

Richard Owen, meanwhile, went on to found the Natural History Museum. But scientific history now views Owen as a liar and a chancer, albeit a talented one. Mantell is revered as the greatest practical pioneer of palaeontology. His family motto was *nil desperandum*: never despair. He did sometimes, though, and I wish that on that terrible December morning in 1838 he could have looked forward two hundred years and seen how he is viewed now.

Moment 49:
The Self is an Unending Project
by William Shaw

We meet for tea in the café at the back of Waitrose on Montpelier Road.

I try to imagine her in leather, with spiked heels pressing down on flesh. A whip maybe.

She is short, round-faced, her hair a mass of orange curls. She is bright and bubbly. A nice, well-spoken Berkshire girl.

I found her in Exchange & Mart. The advert said *Relinquish Control!* One exclamation mark. She called herself *The illustrious Madame Eloise*. Exchange & Mart is a good place to advertise, apparently. Mistress Eloise says all the pervs read it. She's given up on the Friday Ad. 'You only get sniffers there.'

'Sniffers?'

'People who call up and talk and just try to keep you on the phone while they...'

'Oh.'

We drink our tea.

She tells me all about what she does. It's more of a mission than a job. She started at university. She talks about the things she does to clients with nipple clamps and strap-ons and needles. About the importance of never laughing. The pot of tea empties.

I had a girlfriend who asked me to spank her. It was on our first date. I was taken aback. I didn't know what to do. I couldn't imagine myself spanking anyone. So I refused. I wasn't sure if that qualified as an act of sadism in itself. I don't know. We ended up going out for several years. She brought up the subject a few more times. I always said I didn't want to do it. I did actually tie her up twice but my heart wasn't in it. When she left me, I was neither surprised, nor heartbroken.

I don't mention this to Eloise, obviously. After morning tea we go to the pub. Mistress Eloise drinks pints. I have a half.

Her phone goes pretty regularly. She has a second phone for personal calls. It rings. I hear only a few 'Yeses' and 'Nos'. 'That's my slave,' she says proudly when she's snapped the phone shut. He has signed a three-month contract with her; he has to ask her permission to do just about anything, she says.

Back in the sunshine on Western Road, she asks, 'Do you want to see my dungeon?'

'OK,' I say.

It's under a jewellery shop in the North Laine. Convenient for the station. People come from all over. You wouldn't know it's there. The door at the back of the shop could be a broom cupboard. You descend down steep dark stairs into a damp, brick-lined room. Eloise seems very pleased with the place.

Against one wall is a huge wooden X. 'My St Andrew's Cross. I made it myself,' she says.

Shadows of feet tread on the pavement grates above. I try and see naked men or women strapped to the cross. A bit of blood, maybe. I can't. Another failure of the imagination.

I once came across a man called Max who liked to tie women up and suspend them from the ceiling; he did it at least twice a week, he said. He took it all very seriously. 'So much of our lives are about implicit power relationships,' he said earnestly. 'It's good to be explicit about it.' I wasn't sure about that.

I remember reading an academic who said it was all about The Self. *Modern Western culture has placed enormous and unprecedented demands on individual selfhood*, he wrote. *The self is an unending project*, he said. It was a beautiful piece of writing. Basically it said, being The Self is just too stressful. It's good to let go.

I don't know. I suspect spanking someone would make me feel more stressed. Did I hurt you too much?

Did I hurt you too little?

I run my fingers down the pine of Mistress Eloise's St Andrew's Cross. 'That's a nice piece of work,' I say, admiring the way she's bolted it together.

'The man in the timber yard wanted to know what I wanted it for,' she giggles.

I walk back up the stairs into the daylight.

When we came in, the shop was empty. Now it seems to have mysteriously filled. This is the moment I remember clearest. Customers looking at me and smirking. I think I hear a titter. *They know what I have been doing.*

Or think they do.

Moment 50:
On the Level
by Ed Siegle

I sit with my back to the wall on a January morning, my refrigerated arse on grass stiff with frost, and take pictures of the dawn on trees which fall about like gravestones in the rising light. Soon there are pink and blue clouds sanded across the sky and seagulls circling, squawking. She walks through the heart of the Level at 8.15, but she doesn't see me smoking with my camera by the wall because the hood of my parka is pulled up. White headphones in her ears, she strides, a new red scarf around her neck.

One February lunchtime, the sky is a brilliant blue, and, though it's a little chilly, there's no excuse for all those coats. To prove the point I fetch a deckchair, don some shorts and a T-shirt and sit in the middle of the Level reading a newspaper. I get a few looks, but there's always a nutter somewhere here. Today it just happens to be me. So engrossed am I in the crossword, I almost miss her walking, barely feet from me, talking on her mobile – to her mother. I can tell by her tone. I lower my paper but she doesn't see it's me.

In March, the verges hum with daffodils, and mums and dads push wobbling kids on bicycles across segments of grass cut like picnic sandwiches, criss-cross through the middle. The Level used to be full of trees, I'm told, but a great storm blew them down. It's just a park to some, but it was always more than a park to us. I try to do handstands on the grass by the hedge, ending up with a muddy face. After a while, I spy her walking across to the lights at the bottom of Southover, arms straining with bags of shopping.

On an April evening, I sit in the rain on a plastic bag, which doesn't keep my arse dry, and the green beetles painted on my parka are soaked black by the rain. She doesn't pass today on the way to her usual yoga class and for a moment I wonder if she spotted me. My Zippo won't spark, my matches are damp and people skirt around me onto the grass when I ask them for a light. Puddles form in the gravel segment and I wonder why they didn't grass that bit. Rain drips from my hood as I stand in the middle of the crossing of paths at the heart of the park. I wonder if anyone has ever been struck by lightning on the Level. This would be the spot.

The bellies are out on an afternoon in May, and students lollop with white chests and pink arms as they kick a ball about. One of them is quite good. Another thinks he's genius, as they say, but the others roll their eyes when he fucks it up. I offer to go in goal, but they say they're fine. I stand at the side, drinking a can, and they pretend I've gone away. That night I sit on a wall photographing the blinking lights of fairground rides which soon will quiver with the screams of youths. I spy toffee apples, candyfloss – and then her silhouette as she loiters on a central path, laughing with Laura as they pass the Tunnel of Love or is it the Ghost Train. I roll a cigarette but they don't see its glow in the dark.

We first met on midsummer's day, so on our anniversary I dance at midnight in a circle of cider cans, skipping fandangos not so light, must be the boots. Waking before dawn, birds twittering in the elms, night sky brightening from behind, shivering soggy with the dew, I have a revelation. The year is turning. All may not be lost. I go home, take a shower, find some clothes that can remember a washing machine, use deodorant, wash my hands, shave with a razor clear of bristles. Later in the day she crosses the Level with shopping again and I bisect her right in the middle of the crossing of paths.

I say, 'Long time no see...'

'Shitting hell!' says she.

She carries on walking.

'Help with your bags?'

'Sod off.'

On a July evening I play flute with a loose group, lined up along the edge of the wall, running through jazz numbers. I wear shorts with braces, my chest bare, a pork-pie hat – a jazzy look. People sit and picnic, or drink, and kids dance with waggling arms. Someone starts to juggle, so we refuse to play until he desists. She walks not far away, and stops – perhaps she doesn't see it's me – so I wave, which is quite hard whilst fluting. She watches for a while, rolls her eyes, then walks off towards Elm Grove.

In August the trees look huge, I'm sure they've grown, and you can tell the leaves would like to jump off and roll on the ground, but it isn't time yet, so they'll just have to wilt in this heat like the rest of us. There's no hiding place on the Level – well, not in the grassy part at least. Given she saw me play the flute, I take to keeping said instrument about my person, aiming to whip it out and strike a tune, should she come by. She doesn't pass at all in August. Perhaps she's on holiday. Perhaps I missed her – I'm not there all the time. I am forced to finger my flute alone.

There is something different about September grass. A wiriness or a weariness. How long does grass live, I wonder? What is the story of a blade of grass? Be sown, avoid the attention of birds, sway a little in the wind – if you are lucky enough to grow. Sooner or later you end up getting mown. I am lying calmly on the grass, my head in my hand, not really looking out for her, when she strolls right up to me.

'Did you send me a CD?' she asks.

'Of what?'

'I think it was meant to be jazz flute.'

'You dig it?' I ask.

'I play it to my friends whenever they come round. They wet themselves.'

'I wrote those tunes for you.'

'That's what I feared.'

'It's in its infancy...'

'Then abort, while there's still hope for all of us.'

October, and the leaves are thinking of turning orange any day, and the trees wave their arms and look towards the sea and cry. I wonder if they can see the sea, perhaps from the highest of their fingertips, but I think better of trying to climb and see. It's a sharp dawn and the tower block of City College is plated gold. As I cross the Level I find her waiting in the middle of the cross.

'I've run out of CDs,' I say.

'Did you paint a turd on my wall?'

'A turd?' I reply. 'No.'

'It looks a lot like a turd.'

'It was meant to be a rune.'

'Please don't tell me what it means.'

'How many blokes paint their feelings on your wall?'

'Blessed few, thank fuck.'

A November night, and stars fight against the orange of the city sky. I'm sitting on the wall drinking a can, thinking about going to Grubbs for a double bacon, when a voice behind me says, 'Fancy finding you here.'

She sits next to me, saying nothing. We watch people walking down the paths. I try to think of something funny to say, but nothing comes. I turn to her and pull down the beetle painted hood of my parka and wait for her lips to do whatever they have in mind.

'I wanted you to know,' they say, 'I'm leaving Brighton.'

'I should never have bought that flute.'

A first December frost has turned the ground a little white, and in the grass you can see the footprints of a few who've wandered from the path. I meander through the frost myself. I take photographs of light on furry white branches. People come and go: a man with a dog, a few kids in school uniform, students on bicycles. I stand in the middle and turn full circle. I wonder if anyone has ever died here, been buried here. I wonder if anyone loves the Level like I do.

Moment 51:
Brighton 1890s-Style
by Nicky Singer

Lunatic Asylum, July 1896
Admission Number 12,321
Name: Evie Anne Crampton
Age: 5 years
Suicidal? No
Dangerous: Yes, she pinches other children
Observation: Patient has been dejected and very restless. 11 grains of chloral hydrate given. The only intelligible words she has uttered are 'mama' and 'bit of cake'. Patient has passed her evacuations in her clothes and bed, and has thrown herself on the floor in a passion when displeased
Diagnosis: Idiocy
Causation: Unknown
Prognosis: Hopeless

Brighton, September 18th 1896
My Dear Mama
    Please do not concern yourself at my intention to invite the two children to Compton Avenue. If you had seen what I have seen – oh Mama, your own sense of moral purposefulness would rise to choke you. It is not just the chloral hydrate they use, they douche the children with freezing water, they purge them, they tie them to the beds. It cannot be right that children of whatever disposition should be treated so. One of the children – Evie – when I looked at her, I couldn't help but think of a violin, Mama. Imagine that a violinist is about to play a beautiful sonata, and that his violin is suddenly damaged by accident. The sonata is just as beautiful, the violinist has lost none of his skill, but neither the beauty of the music nor the violinist's skill can come to expression, because the instrument is damaged. It is the same with the handicapped child. The bodily instrument is damaged, but the individuality is nevertheless still

there. That's what we should never lose sight of.
My love
Grace

Mama,
   You were right: there were difficulties and tantrums, and some willful tearing of leaves from the aspidistra, but I forgot it all when I took the children to the Esplanade. Maud, who is thought to be about seven years old, was all for rushing straight onto the beach, but Evie just stood, as if amazed. Then, casting a hand towards the ocean, she said: 'Sea.' Said it with such intensity, such vehemence that I thought, for a moment, that she had not named the sea but created it. These are the children, Mama, that I must return to the Asylum tomorrow.
Grace

Board of Control Meeting, May 4th 1932
   Chairman, we wish to register our alarm at the large number of mental defectives which are being imported into Brighton from other areas. We believe that the steadily increasing number of defectives is a grave menace to the amenities of the Town as a health Resort and submit that, unless prompt measures are taken to severely control this importation, the status and reputation of Brighton, the preservation of which is vital to the life of the town, will be severely prejudiced.'
   'Miss Woodhead?'
   'Nonsense.'

Brighton, April 12th 1928
Mama
   I am not to be put aside by the Board of Control now. We now have 850 patients in the care of the society, 100 under supervision in their own homes and 750 boarded out in caring placements. You may like to know how the education of the 'ineducable' is proceeding. It is a job indeed that requires endless patience. The children at the day centre were the other day drawing and colouring circles. The teacher explained that the circles were round, like an orange. When, a few minutes later, one child was asked what he was drawing, he cheerfully replied, 'a banana'.
Grace

Board of Control, November 4th 1931

I personally examined the alleged defective – John Morrell – and satisfied myself that he was category 'b' – an imbecile. His expression is vacant. His articulation is defective. He understands very little of what is said to him.

With regards to bodily health, he has a malformation of the left forearm, and only three fingers on each hand.

Brighton, September 10th 1931

My dear Hilda

There's a little boy. His name is John Morrell, an illegitimate child, just four years old. His eyes are very far away, but also deep. I wonder what he thinks. He will be placed with Millicent Wade, so I have high hopes for him. The work must go on Hilda, when I do not. Grace.

And so the work did and does. 60 years after, Grace Eyre Woodhead was buried at All Saints Church, Hove, John Morrell was still under the Guardianship of the Society. I met him at the day centre in Avondale Road. He didn't know who Grace Eyre was. He was working a figure in clay. He said it was an image of Christ. He'd given it just three fingers.

Moment 52:
Fish out of Water
by Gilly Smith

Day One of my trip back to the days when shopping was a social activity and food still had its head on, and the supermarket is already a distant memory. I've left the car in the multi-storey and am strolling through the rain to the market, reusable bag (Soil Association logo facing out) in hand, and I can't remember when I've felt so excited about buying fresh fish.

The fishmonger, as leathery faced and smelly as I remember fishmongers of my youth, is shooing flies away from the open-jawed aliens of the deep whose body parts I've been happily grilling for the past twenty-five years without a clue as to where they came from. Now, I'm going local. I'm thinking baked mackerel for lunch and a cod pie for supper. Remembering Jamie Oliver's advice, I take a sniff. 'Oh, no you don't,' says the fishmonger. 'If you can't see that it's fresh by looking at it, you should go to the supermarket.' Horrified, I put it down quickly and ask sheepishly if he has a wet wipe. Fishmongers seem much friendlier in Sainsbury's.

I feel a fraud. He's right; I am one of those Johnny-come-latelies who have watched too much Jamie Oliver and think we can save the world by shopping locally and seasonally. But as I slope away, I want to stamp my foot and tell him about my childhood summers of crab filled rock-pools, of campsite suppers, pulling our foraged mussels from their shells and mopping up the sea-salty white wine sauce with a hunk of local bread, of barbecued mackerel swapped for next-to-nothing from the local fishermen bringing their boats in with that day's catch. I want to tell him my family's stories of the Saturday morning door-to-door visits by the women from Penclawdd who would carry their cockles in baskets perched on their heads.

The years between those countryside summers of the 70s and my city-based parenting have been largely shrink-wrapped instead of line-caught, and I've brought my kids up on a diet of Mediterranean goodness rather than local, seasonal produce. My kids' idea of a coastline is Brighton Pier and their relationship with animals is based on their eight rabbits, two hamsters, two cats and an ageing dog. My eldest is more likely to liberate a crab from Shoreham Fish Market than snap its claw and suck out the flesh. I blame the parents. Perhaps it's time to take them fishing.

Ernie the Fish, whose little boat has been bringing home the catch from Newhaven for more years than he cares to remember, agrees to take us out. The September morning is a stunner, the sea a glassy green, and the kids are already telling me that this is the best day of their lives. I've done it; putting a few twenties in the palm of an old seadog has awarded me the crown I gave my father for strapping crochet hooks to the old broomsticks we used to winkle out our crab dinner from those rock-pools, and I haven't even got my feet wet. I sit smugly and watch my nature-girls and their gang of mates move like eels about the boat, studying Ernie as he prepares their rods, even picking up a wriggling ragworm and skewering it with their shiny hooks, eager to cast their line.

An hour later, the tide has turned. Our little boat, which had been puttering on gentle waves for the first few miles, is now rearing wildly on walls of water as if trying to dump the secret supermarket shoppers it has spotted within. My girls have long since crawled into little green-gilled balls and, mercifully, are sleeping through this freak storm, but their father is fighting with twelve-year-old seasick Sam for the mackerel bucket after being hurled against the side of the boat. I think he may even be concussed.

As our brutalised little army heads home, the sun shines again, and Ernie stoically suggests to the few of us still standing that we cast our rods and see if we can save the day. The low throb of the engine is the only sound as the worms wriggle and hooks glisten in the dead calm of the English Channel, until Sam throws the last of his breakfast over the side. Suddenly the rods are bucking and bending, children are screaming as the sea comes alive with fish grabbing at Sam's Coco-Pops, and my sleeping girls wake up wondering what happened to their perfect day. One of the dads clings to his five-year-old as his rod threatens to pull him over the edge and there are cheers now as mackerel after mackerel is reeled in and flung on deck. Ernie's smile has made my day.

Back home, gloves and aprons on, the girls watch solemnly as we gut the fish and lay them on the barbecue. As the skin toasts and shrinks to reveal the perfect white meaty flesh, I pass one to each of my little fishermen, my body language unable quite to conceal my empty hope. Politely they decline, skip off to grab a sandwich at someone else's house, and I am left with thirty-six mackerels staring at me, wondering which of us has won.

The Route of the Arrow
by David Swann

It was midnight at the end of a long, humid June day and I was heading home up Elm Grove, the long tree-lined avenue that connects Brighton to its race course.

In the distance, someone was shouting angrily, but I dismissed it as the usual outpourings from the malign local lay-line that is sometimes mistakenly called London Road.

It had grown dark now under the elms, and muggy, and I was switching a heavy satchel from shoulder to shoulder as I traipsed up the hill. The satchel contained dozens of poems and stories by life prisoners whom I had taught. The work was to become an anthology and was currently at proof stage, its pages scarred by the red ink that I'd applied in my role as editor.

Earlier that day, I'd used the prisoners' work to illustrate a one-off session on writing and freedom at a local university. It had come as a refreshing change to be invited to teach in a peaceful environment, without the roar of confined men in the background, and I was reflecting upon the experience as I trudged up Elm Grove, watching the first shivers of summer lightning pass across the sky.

In the moments before the attack happened, I dimly recall that I was also thinking of trees, for Elm Grove is rich in them, its steep gradient a purpose-built parade route for the dead of Brighton, who are saluted by the elms on their final journey up the hill to the graveyard.

Back then, I was preoccupied by trees, since the jail had been planted in a clearing near Sherwood in Nottingham, where the outlaw Robin Hood is said to have roamed the forests.

The jail had only two trees, one a spindly ash next to the topping shed, the other a huge and beautiful cherry tree that spread its boughs over the prison yard.

Men had once been put to death in the topping shed. Hence, its name. I was told that bodies still lay buried at the base of the ash. 'Even in death they couldn't escape.' As for the cherry tree, I'd watched workers drive a camera pole through its core. 'Rape,' one of the men called it.

During my year at the jail, I'd often found myself staring into the vast places within the cherry tree. It was separated from Sherwood by a high wall, beyond which there was no longer a forest. There had been something about the plight of this tree that reminded me of the prisoners I taught.

Maybe I also had more prosaic things on my mind as I traipsed home up the hill – the work on the satchel of proofs that awaited me, the struggle to find a job that provided enough to live on while continuing to write.

Whatever I was truly thinking vaporised as soon as I saw the ashen-faced man hurling beer bottles into the driveway of the local primary school.

His girlfriend clung to the school railings, clutching a toddler to her chest. The toddler howled in terror while she screamed at her boyfriend to stop.

The man did not stop. He went on ripping bottle after bottle from a carrier bag and hurling each of them into the gateway. The noise that came out of him while he did this was the most frightening I've ever heard. It was the roar of some forest beast, some dreadful thing gored by a trap. He was screaming so hard that his lips had turned blue, that his eyes seemed about to burst from their skull.

I was frightened, even, by his hair, a fierce buzz-cut that laid bare a bolt of bone across the back of his head. He was like a door that had been sealed from outside. We were stuck inside his rage with him, no way out.

When I attempted eye contact with his girlfriend, she shrank from my gaze and tightened her grip on the toddler. The toddler squirmed like a fish in a net, opening its lungs to gasp, gone beyond screaming into a racked silence. When I look back now, I see the child's eyes, I see the summer lightning that trembled beyond the trees.

Earlier that evening, I had talked about outlaws and arrows. I'd told the university students what jail had taught me: that certain men are like arrows, fired many years ago and falling to earth ever since. I'd learned that nothing can stop these arrows from falling, and that the only defence is to avoid the place where the arrow lands.

Now I had come to that place.

I said to the man: 'Steady, mate. Go easy. The school-kids...'

He'd hit me before I even saw him raise his hand. And I was down in the broken glass suffering his kicks while his fingers seemed still to be curling into a fist.

Who did I think I was, he asked me.

Who.

Did.

I.

Think.

I.

Was.

With each blow, I flew further from pain. The only experience I can compare it to is being rolled by an Atlantic wave. You don't know which way is up, which way is down. The roar of the ocean surrounds your body, but you are somehow separate from it. You have fallen into a gap between two worlds.

Then, somehow, I'd been flung clear and was wedged in a stand of privet bushes, using my satchel as a shield while he threw down punch after punch and I begged him to stop and his girlfriend screamed and the toddler burst free from her grip and toppled into the broken glass.

But I no longer cared about the child because the man had hit the satchel so hard that its catch had exploded and the prisoners' work was blowing free across the road. And he had taken a broken bottle in his fist and was telling me exactly how he intended to punish me for coming between him and his family. A private matter. And his voice had taken on a lower, more controlled, tone.

'Want some, do you. Want some.'

'Please,' I said. 'Your child...'

Lightning flashed through the trees behind him. It sounds like a cliché to say this. But all violence is a cliché, anyway. That's what I remember thinking as he stood above me under the lovely darkness of the elms with the broken bottle cocked like a gun in his fist. All violence is a cliché, anyway.

How I stumbled free, I don't recall. Why he chose to batter me from then on with his left hand rather than the hand with the bottle, I have no idea. At one stage, I remember grovelling in the road for the prisoners' proofs while he kicked me, and stuffing the pages into my broken satchel, and realising that my attacker had cut his fist on its buckle, and his blood was dripping off my chin.

But then I was bolting up the hill past the Exhaust & Battery

Centre, trying to breathe again, muttering my shame under my breath while he screamed somewhere behind me that there was no point running because he knew exactly where I lived.

And what hurt most was the exultant tone in his voice and the thought that I had given him exactly what he wanted and the memory of being squashed inside a stupid bush, and how I'd grovelled in the dirt while he kicked me.

And, although I later tried to comfort myself by putting it down to the injustice of a country where the rich are too rich and the poor too poor, and the schizophrenia of a town which is equal parts soother and savage, I knew I wasn't kidding myself.

For there isn't any comfort for a grown man who has been humiliated like a child in the street, not even when he bursts through the front door of his home and submits to the tenderness of his wife.

Contributors:

Will Ainley lives in Brighton and is a member of Scrawl Collective, a global group of illustrators and designers. He creates limited edition prints and T-shirt designs of his work. His clients include Penguin Books, EMI Records, Time Out Magazine and Howies.

David Bramwell has written books on subjects ranging from alcohol to sexuality but is probably best-known locally as the creator of the *Cheeky Guide to Brighton* for which he continues to be praised and vilified in equal measure. He lives in Hanover.

Paul Burgess trained as a textiles designer at the Royal College of Art and has worked as an illustrator, designer, photographer, artist and writer. He is the author of *Satellite: Sex Pistols Graphic Design and Memorabilia* and is an advisor to Sotheby's on Punk Graphics and Clothing.

Graham Carter has worked as an illustrator and printmaker for over ten years. He studied at the University of Brighton and Central St. Martin's, London. He exhibits his work in the UK and Europe frequently and has created illustrations for a range of clients including Bupa, Orange and Visa.

Madeleine Cary worked in television and film for many years. Her short stories and essays have been published in *Women Travel, Soul Providers, The Ex-Files Anthology,* BBC Radio 4 and in various magazines. She has been short-listed twice for the Ian St James Award.

Astrid Chesney studied illustration at the University of Brighton and went on to study at the Royal College of Art. Astrid's work draws on the everyday, people and places. She has worked with Time Magazine Asia, the New York Times, Random House, Hodder & Stoughton, Oberon Books, and major national newspapers.

Rose Collis has lived in Sussex since 1997. Her work includes *Brighton Boozers* at the Brighton Museum & Art Gallery and The Icons Project. Her books include *A Trouser-Wearing Character: The Life and Times of Nancy Spain, Colonel Barker's Monstrous Regiment,* and *Coral Browne: 'This Effing Lady'.*

Miles Donovan studied at the University of Brighton and has over ten years' experience as an illustrator. As co-founder of Peepshow, an illustration collective, he has worked on design, art direction and animation projects for the BBC, Nike, Channel Four, Coca-Cola, Toyota, Diesel and the Victoria and Albert Museum.

Peter James Field studied world art history and anthropology before studying and practising as an illustrator. Born in Scotland, he grew up in Poole and whilst studying at the University of Brighton chose to live in Hove, rather than Brighton. His clients include Dazed and Confused, Time Out and Carlos magazines.

David Foldvari was born in Budapest but has lived in the UK for over twenty years. His work is bold, dark and often political. Previous clients include: the New York Times, Greenpeace, Random House, Dazed & Confused and Island Records. He won a D&AD award for work on Nike's 'Run London' and Beck's 'The Information.'

Jason Ford studied graphic design and illustration in Brighton and then at the Royal College of Art, where he gained his MA. He has exhibited his work internationally and works regularly for clients across the editorial, publishing, design and advertising fields. His work has won Association of Illustrators awards.

Katy Gardner lives near Lewes. She is the author of three novels (*Losing Gemma*, 2001, *The Mermaid's Purse*, 2003, *Hidden*, 2006) and various works of non-fiction. Katy teaches social anthropology at the University of Sussex.

Marian Garvey won First Prize in the Asham Award 2007 for *All That's Left*, and was short-listed in 2005 and 2006. Three of her stories were long-listed for the Fish Prize in 2005. Her story *Don't Turn Round* was broadcast on BBC Radio 4. Marian is currently completing a collection of short stories and is working on her first novel.

Annabel Giles has been a model, TV and radio presenter, actress and comedienne. Highlights from those careers include an exclusive contract with Max Factor, being a regular reporter on *Loose Ends* and writing herself a one-woman sell-out show at the Edinburgh Festival. She has also written three novels for the bitter and twisted.

Jasper Goodall has been described as one of the most influential graphic artists of his generation. Despite being widely imitated he has constantly reinvented his work. He has worked for numerous clients, creating a range of limited edition prints and a range of luxury swimwear. He teaches illustration at the University of Brighton.

Peter Guttridge's six comic novels were published an embarrassingly long time ago. He is currently working on a non-comic Brighton trilogy, the first of which, *The City of Dreadful Night*, will be published when he can stop fiddling with it.

Professor George Hardie worked closely with Hipgnosis, creating sleeves for Pink Floyd, Led Zeppelin and Black Sabbath. George has worked with clients internationally and has created stamps for the Royal Mail. He is a member of the Alliance Graphique Internationale, Double Crown Club and Artworkers Guild and teaches at the University of Brighton.

Carole Hayman is well-known as co-writer of the BBC Radio 4 hit series *Ladies of Letters*. Her films have been shown at festivals worldwide and her journalism published in major newspapers. Carole's last novel, *Hard Choices*, was short-listed for the Silver Booker and her new novel, *The Rashomon Principle*, will be published in 2008.

Margaret Huber lectures in illustration. Her ongoing visual diary project, *Day Trip to Brighton*, a collection of close to a thousand drawings on used train tickets from her daily commute from London, was one of a series of works shown in an exhibition of her work, *Telling Stories*, at Minneapolis College of Arts and Design.

Oliver Hydes lives and works in Brighton. He has exhibited as part of the Open Houses in the Brighton Festival and has a client-base that includes the Observer, Three's Company and Visit London. He creates a weekly illustration on a current news topic and continues to work on self-initiated art and design projects.

Susanna Jones has published three novels, *The Earthquake Bird*, *Water Lily*, and *The Missing Person's Guide to Love*. Her work is widely translated and has won a CWA dagger, a Betty Trask award and the John Llewellyn Rhys Prize. She teaches creative writing at Royal Holloway, London University.

Marek Kohn's latest book, *Trust*, will be published by OUP in 2008. His previous book, *A Reason for Everything: Natural Selection and the English Imagination*, included a biographical account of the distinguished Sussex University evolutionary biologist John Maynard Smith.

Martine McDonagh lives and works in Brighton. Her first novel, *I Have Waited, and You Have Come*, was published in 2007.

Joe McLaren is an artist and illustrator. His work combines drawing and painting techniques with traditional printmaking working methods to create simple yet beautifully iconic images across illustration and artist book projects.

Alison MacLeod grew up in Canada and has lived in England since 1987. She has published two novels, *The Changeling* and *The Wave Theory of Angels*, and a story collection, *Fifteen Modern Tales of Attraction*. She teaches English and Creative Writing at the University of Chichester and is working on her new novel, set in Brighton.

Marine was born in Paris, grew up in the South of France and moved to Brighton to study graphic design. Now living and working in Brighton as an illustrator, she divides her time between commissions for the Guardian, Design Week, Amelia's Magazine and Time Out, and personal work that she exhibits regularly.

Asako Masunouchi has been a freelance illustrator and animator since 2005 when she graduated from the University of Brighton. Based in Japan she mainly works on magazines, books and CD jackets for international clients. She is interested in the humorous and melancholic elements of everyday life.

Roderick Mills has won awards for his illustration and animation work and has exhibited his work internationally. He studied at the Royal College of Art and has a client-base across publishing, editorial, advertising and corporate literature. He has worked with the Royal Mail, the BBC, the National Theatre, Volkswagen and New York Magazine.

Dan Mumford is an illustrator/designer/screenprint artist based in London. He has designed record and CD sleeve designs for indie rockers Gallows, and created illustrations and T-shirt designs for a growing international client-base.

Tanya Murray used to be a man but gave it up. Her boyfriend took it well. He moved to Australia. In her day job as a Detective Sergeant she investigates the sins of other cops. At least one of these facts accounts for her always managing to get a table to herself in the police canteen.

Jeff Noon was born in Manchester. He was musically active in the punk scene before starting to write plays. Since his first novel, *Vurt*, published in 1993, he has concentrated on applying ideas and methods from musical composition to narrative. His other books include *Automated Alice*, *Pixel Juice*, *Needle in the Groove* and *Falling Out Of Cars*.

Jed Novick has worked for several national newspapers as a feature writer, critic and editor. He has set up three national magazines and has written ten books: two on football, two on music, four biographies - including the first authorised biography of Michael Palin - and two books on sex.

Sally O'Reilly has written two comic novels. *The Best Possible Taste* is the story of a Brighton chef who tries to apply perfection to life and food, and ends up getting divorced and eating rubbish take-aways. *You Spin Me Round* is the account of an accidental Greenham sister in the 80s. Sally lives in Hanover.

Chris Paling is the author of eight novels, the latest of which is *Minding*. He has written for radio and the national press and works full-time as a radio producer. He is married with two children, lives in Brighton and is currently writing his ninth novel which may or may not be called *Nimrod's Shadow*.

Gary Powell has worked on projects spanning editorial, design, advertising and multimedia. His work was selected for the Royal Mail's Millennium Stamp Collection. Awards include a D&AD Yellow Pencil Silver Award and the B&H First Gold Pencil Award for Illustration. Powell became a patron of the Association of Illustrators in 1999.

Corinna Radcliffe describes her work as 'vibrant, feminine and full of pattern'. She lives and works in Brighton but much of her inspiration comes from her travels in Cuba, Thailand and Morocco. She draws from the imagery and patterns found in temples and the Islamic patterns seen all over Morocco.

Sue Roe's most recent books are *Gwen John: A Life* and *The Private Lives of the Impressionists*, which has been translated into six languages. Her poetry is widely published in journals and anthologies including *New Poetries III* (Carcanet) and *Agenda*. She teaches creative writing at the University of Sussex.

Nicholas Royle is Professor of English at the University of Sussex. He has written two novels and numerous short stories. His books include *Telepathy and Literature* (1990) and *The Uncanny* (2003). He is Joint-Editor of the Oxford Literary Review.

C. J. Sansom studied history at Birmingham University. He is the author of the acclaimed historical crime series featuring lawyer Matthew Shardlake. The fourth in the series, *Revelation*, was published in April 2008. He also wrote the best-selling *Winter in Madrid*, set in Franco's Spain.

Natsko Seki is an illustrator, animator and graphic designer. Born in Japan and trained at the University of Brighton, her work combines upbeat and humorous ideas. Natsko has worked with clients as diverse as Muji, the New York Times, the London Fire Brigade and Hankyu Department Store in Japan.

William Shaw is the author of *Spying in Guru Land*, an account of a year spent as a member of six different religious cults, and *Westsiders – Stories of the Boys in the Hood*, about young men growing up in South Central LA. *41 Places: 41 Stories* was a collection based on his site-specific story exhibition *41 Places* (Brighton Festival 2007). He runs the imprint Unmadeup.

Ed Siegle was born and bred in Somerset, and has lived in Brighton for six years. He is the author of two unpublished novels, *Killing a Friend* and *Invisibles,* and has written a number of short stories, one of which, *Nine Lives, One Life,* won the 2004 VS Pritchett Memorial Prize.

Nicky Singer writes novels for adults and young people and has written two books of non-fiction. *Feather Boy* won the Blue Peter Book of the Year Award and was adapted for television. Nicky is writing the libretto for a youth opera (based on her forthcoming novel *The Knight Crew*) to be premiered at Glyndebourne in 2010.

Gilly Smith has written for several major national newspapers and magazines, specialising in food, kids, health and green issues. She has had nine books published, mainly about food, and published *The Juicy Guide to Brighton and Hove* for four years. She teaches Writing for Media at the University of Brighton.

Alice Stevenson studied illustration at the University of Brighton. She has created illustrations for various clients, including Faber and Faber, Puffin and Time Out, and is a regular contributor to the Guardian. Alice's work has also been reproduced on wrapping paper, greetings cards and furnishing fabric.

Jim Stoten works across illustration, art, printmaking and street drawing projects. Recent trips to Berlin and New York have seen collaborations with artists and designers in both cities. Jim works regularly for the Guardian, Amelia's Magazine and Cream.

David Swann was born up the street from his childhood neighbour Jeanette Winterson and used to cover Accrington Stanley's matches for the local rag. The author of prize-winning poems and stories, David now teaches English at the University of Chichester. His collection *The Last Days of Johnny North* was published in 2006.

Lucy Vigrass studied illustration at the University of Brighton and was a founding member of illustration collective Peepshow. Lucy works on illustration and animation commissions and projects and on her own limited-edition prints. Her clients include Penguin Books, the New York Times, and the Sunday Telegraph.

Hannah Waldren works with ideas across a range of applications which include animation, illustration, art direction, craft and photography. She has also created limited edition screen-prints and launched the beginnings of her own range of accessories.

Steve Wilson lives and works in Brighton as an illustrator, creating contemporary images that have their roots in 1970s rock and pop and 1980s New York style. Steve's work has been commissioned for clients such as MTV, Wallpaper, Selfridges, Coca Cola and Virgin Digital.

Matt Wingfield studied Graphic Design before embarking on MA Textiles at the Royal College of Art. He previously headed the in-house design department at Harvey Nichols in London and now works primarily in retail graphics and illustrations. Matt's recent projects include work for Topshop, Liberty, Monsoon and Ted Baker.

Ian Wright's first commission was designing the cover of the Undertones' *Teenage Kicks* 7-inch single. He created weekly black-and-white portraits for the New Musical Express in the 1980s and has created installations for Issey Miyake, Brinkworth Architects, Milliken Carpet, Vitra and the Design Council.

Lawrence Zeegen is an academic, illustrator and design writer. A graduate of the Royal College of Art, he runs courses in Graphic Design and Illustration at the University of Brighton, has a regular illustration slot in the Guardian, is a contributing writer for Computer Arts magazine, has written three books on contemporary illustration, with two more forthcoming, and has lectured internationally on design education and contemporary illustration.

About Unmadeup
Unmadeup is a not-for-profit publishing company based in Brighton, which was set up in 2007 to specialise in creating and publishing new non-fiction forms. Previous work includes the installation 41 Places by William Shaw (www.41places.org). Find out more by visiting www.unmadeup.com.

THE SHADOWE

CHOKEPOINT

CHRIS LOWRY

CHRIS LOWRY

Chokepoint a Shadowboxer File

Contents

1

CHAPTER ONE

XALATAN — SOUTHEAST MEXICO

Southeast Mexico is a weird place. The beaches are gorgeous and undiscovered, archaeological marvels dot the landscape and even more are hidden under the green canopy of verdant jungle that stretches down to the border with Central America.

The desert marches from Texas and New Mexico across the flat expanse to butt up against the edge of the jungle to bleed brown scrub and yellow sand into the green thick plant life.

Xalatan was a small city on what was generously called a highway that catered to the beach bound tourists. It was a jumping off point for tours into the jungle to see monuments of the past, a haven for surfers and wayfarers making an adventurous trip across the continent.

Juan's was a dive bar off of a back alley that was simple four walls and a tin roof.

The bar was made from an expensive looking jungle hardwood, probably harvested almost a hundred years ago with the smooth sweat stained top that comes from a lot of elbows and arms propped against the edge.

The walls were adorned with cheap beer promotions, the shelves behind the bar had an assortment of shot glasses, beer mugs and a couple of tequila tumblers. Almost all of them had small cracks or chips.

The door was propped open with a chair, the windows were folded up and chained to the roof in an effort to catch any breeze that might stir the fetid air inside. Two bamboo leaf ceiling fans were connected by a rubber belt, so that when one turned it caused the other to turn with it.

Old worn tables were scattered around the room in no apparent pattern, some with three chairs on the sides. Two men sat at one of the tables engrossed in a chessboard and an almost empty fifth of tequila that rested between them.

Brill Winger was five eleven and almost forgettable. His face was handsome in a plain fashion, what could be seen of it behind a thick beard. His hair was long and drawn in a ponytail that rested between muscular shoulder blades hidden under a loose white shirt.

A man almost his polar opposite sat across from him and glared under a thick brow with piggish eyes.

Where Brill was athletic and ripped, Johnson was a man who took his pleasure to excess. He topped the scales at three hundred pounds and stood almost six inches taller than Brill.

He had a balding pate with a fringe of hair trimmed short and he was clean shaven. His baby face that made him look younger than he actually was, but the perpetual scowl was meant to keep people away.

"You're up," said Brill.

Johnson took a shot glass full of amber tequila and slurped it down. He set it on the chessboard in a new position among the rest of the empty shot glasses.

"Check," he slurred.

Brill lifted an almost empty bottle of tequila in a steady hand and tipped the last drops into a shot glass.

"That was a gutsy move."

Johnson mopped his sweaty head with a frayed rag.

"I thought you might like it."

Brill rolled the bottle across the floor. It clinked against the bar.

"Barkeep! Another."

"Who calls them barkeep anymore? You think this is the wild wild west?"

"What would you call him? Bartender? Keeper of the bottle? Server of the tequila and whiskey and wine? He sets the bar high by keeping the bar to serve us until we're low. Hence, barkeep. Pour us another one, we're finished with the other one."

"You're not gonna need it."

"That's tough talk from a man in your position."

"You can only make two moves. It's a classic offense."

Brill sat up and studied the table with bleary eyes. The grease stained Barkeep gently set a fresh bottle of tequila beside him.

"What do you think of this?"

The barkeep studied the dirty chessboard and shrugged. He walked back behind the bar and turned up the boom box. He pretended to wipe down the glasses with a grime covered rag.

"What's your name again?" Brill asked his opponent.

"Johnson. Cooper Johnson. My friends call me Digger."

He stuck out a sweaty paw that Brill shook. It was limp in his hand.

"Not Coop?"

"Nope, Digger. That's what they called my grandfather and after he died, they said I looked like him, so the family started calling me Digger."

"You look like your dead grandfather, Coop? I don't know if that's a good thing."

"Your mind games won't work on me friend. I mean when he was alive."

"I don't know if that's a marked improvement," Brill smirked. "It could be the tequila though."

"Let's blame the tequila and save my pride."

"I can agree to that. Do you know what I do in situations like this, Cooper Digger Coop?"

"Admit defeat and surrender gracefully?"

Brill smiled. He uncorked the bottle and took two long swallows before he pushed it across to Johnson.

"I'll be back."

"Where you going?"

Brill grabbed his crotch.

"Digger, we just met and I'm not that easy on a first date."

Johnson waved him off.

"Clock's ticking.

"I know."

Johnson watched him stumble to the dark hallway that led to the back of the bar.

4

2

CHAPTER TWO

Brill nudged the bathroom door open with the toe of his hiking boots. The wood, caked from years of greasy beer soaked fingers, was three shades of black where patrons had touched it. It looked toxic.

Inside was worse. The small space had a toilet and two urinals in a length of five feet. It looked like any two people doing their business would be forced to stand toe to toe to get it done. The floor was an amalgamation of misses, near misses and deliberate soakings, combined to create a stinking cesspool of waste.

A small window above the back of the toilet offered the only potential relief.

It was edged open. He shoved against it gently and pushed the crack open two inches. Brill reached into one of the baggy pockets on the side of his cargo pants and pulled out a sleek pistol. From the other pocket he produced a three-inch silencer he screwed on the end of the pistol.

He rested the pistol against the edge of the window and peered out at the road. He checked his watch and waited.

The bartender banged on the door.

"Why you got it locked? There's room in there."

"Be out in a minute," Brill called.

He turned his focus back to the window.

A long black Cadillac rolled into view. Diplomatic flags fluttered on the hood of the car. The windows were tinted, but one rear window was half way down. A cloud of cigar smoke filtered out in a blue smog.

Brill sighted down the end of the pistol and pulled the trigger twice. A misshapen head bounced against the car window and rested there. The car screeched to a stop.

Brill shoved the gun in his waistband and shouldered through the door.

"Ain't you gonna wash your hands," the bartender asked in a thick accent.

"Sorry," Brill moved past him down the hall.

3

CHAPTER THREE

Brill strolled to the table and grabbed a shot glass. He swallowed the tequila and set the glass down to a new spot on the board.

Johnson smiled as he swilled down a shot of tequila and set his piece in place.

"Checkmate," he grunted.

Brill dropped a crumpled twenty-dollar bill onto the table.

"Good game," he said.

"Let's make it two?"

The front door crashed open and four giant thugs ran through. They were dressed in matching khaki uniforms, huge swaths of fabric stretched tight over giant muscles. They raced toward the back of the bar.

"Too crowded," said Brill. "Maybe next time."

He lowered his head and walked slowly out of the door. One of the thugs with a unibrow noticed him and moved to intercept.

Brill slipped past him and out of the door. He mingled with a passing crowd of tourists that skirted around the Caddy parked half on the curb. The thug tried to find him in the mass of people, but Brill kept his head low and blended in. He made the next corner and turned away from the people.

4

CHAPTER FOUR

The phone booth seemed like a quiet oasis in the crowded chaos of the tourist clogged city street. The side facing the sidewalk had two windows missing so the noise washed over and echoed inside the glass chamber.

Brill stood in the booth, dressed like a tourist. His beard had been shaved into a modified goatee and damp hair curled against his neck.

"I'm on a land line. Confirm. This is Shadowboxer. Target rendered ineffective."

The glass above his head shattered. He ran from the booth, shoved open a shop door. A bullet thudded into his left shoulder. He spun into the room and kicked the door shut behind him.

The room was a crowed knick-knack shop full of cheap local goods mass produced in China. Mountains of tee shirts spilled off wobbly tables, stone and clay renderings of ziggurat, Mayan gods and sea creatures fought for shelf space.

Brill shuffled to one of the tables.

He grabbed a hooded poncho, an oversized straw hat, a blanket and tee shirt and carried them to the counter.

With one hand held close to his side, he fished a ten dollar and twenty-dollar bill out of his pocket and set it on the counter.

"No bag," he grunted in Spanish.

He used one hand to arrange the poncho over his head, and perched the straw hat on his brow.

"Is there a back way?"

The clerk ignored the register and pocketed the bills.

"Through the doors."

He waved another twenty under her nose.

"I'm in the bathroom."

She swiped the note, and secreted it with the others. Brill moved through the doors. He packed his shoulder with the tee shirt to staunch the bleeding.

"Hey!" said the Clerk.

Brill turned, a small 9mm in his hand. She glanced down at the gun and tossed him two more shirts, her finger crooked toward a handwritten sign above the table that read, 3 FOR $10.

"Special."

She winked. He smiled, slipped through the door, hidden under the poncho and a hat.

5

CHAPTER FIVE

Brill walked down the alley close to the wall. He stopped at the street, and did a scan. Everything appeared normal. A large group of tourists waddled past on their way to a bus. Brill fell in step with them and eased into the center of the crowd.

The group bottlenecked at the bus, but Brill moved past them to the next corner and disappeared.

CHAPTER SIX

Someone watched the hat and poncho disappear around a corner. Two men stood on a rooftop several blocks away. One lay prone on the roof, a rifle butt pressed to his shoulder, his eye against the scope. He was in his thirties, thick muscles with a layer of a few years of comfortable living around them. He had sandy brown hair and hazel eyes. The second man stood next to him.

It wasn't the most inconspicuous spot to be in, he presented a good target silhouetted against the sky. He held himself with confidence, legs wide as if braced on the deck of a ship. His hair was gray with flecks of black, his eyes were blue, and once upon a time, he may have been handsome, though gravity and gravitas conspired to darken his glower. He was trim to the point of being built like a long-distance runner. Corded muscles stood out on his arms and flexed as he tracked with binoculars.

"There he goes," said the standing man.

"I swear I hit him Foster."

Foster dropped the binoculars to the roof deck.

"I've no doubt, my friend."

"I must have winged him. Or, he's got a vest. Did he wear a vest with you?"

"I believe you, Wallace. If you say you hit him, then he is indeed hit."

"But not down."

"No. A wounded animal becomes much more dangerous, yes. But wounded we may stand a chance. He will go to ground in a safe house."

His voice was cultured and elegant, tinged with a slight British accent. Foster pointed to the crowd below.

"After you make a shot, watch the crowd. When you shoot someone in public, the crowds going to do two things. Either they will duck and run for cover, or they're going to run for a look. You do what the rest of them are doing. If you walk away calmly, someone's going to notice. And if they notice, they might tell."

The rooftop stairwell door burst open and four soldiers rushed through. They had assault rifles held high and screamed in Spanish.

Foster whipped a pistol from behind his back and dropped them with one shot each.

Wallace glanced up at his mentor.

Foster shrugged and held a satellite radio to his ear.

"Secured transmission. This is Killjoy. Hut location?"

"Confirmed," said a tinny voice over the speaker. "Will deliver."

"Pack up, we're moving north."

Wallace broke down the rifle and stored the components in slim black backpack filled with cut foam.

"How confident are you he will go there?"

"What else can he do?"

7

CHAPTER SEVEN

There are a few vehicles that are iconic in Third World countries. Toyota Land Cruisers crisscross the African Savannah with reliable regularity, Nissan Pick Up Trucks dot the Middle Eastern landscape like automotive camels. In Mexico, it's the VW. The VW Bug and its counterpart, the VW Bus putter along Mexican highways and clog up side streets due to huge mass production two decades ago and an interchangeability of parts in the easy to repair engines.

One of those iconic buses puttered along the edge of a jungle on a dusty highway. Veronica James had one hand on the steering wheel, one leg crossed under the other in the seat and a perpetual smile. She was dressed in khaki shorts, a button up shirt, and looked like what she was, a free-spirited archeology student, still dirty from a dig.

The van was packed with the debris of long travel, clothes, a sleeping mat and bag, food wrappers and a couple of beer bottles that rolled around on the back floor.

Ron sang off key to a song on the radio. She rounded a corner and swerved left to avoid a man on the side of the road. He weaved along the edge, but stuck his thumb out in the classic hitchhikers pose.

Ron slowed down and watched him in the rear-view mirror for a moment. She pulled over to the side of the road and waited. While she waited, she opened the glove box and pulled out a small dull silver .22 and stuck it under her leg so it was hidden from the door.

The passenger door swung open and the man used one arm to haul himself in to collapse on the seat.

"Thanks for stopping," he grunted. "I thought I might have to walk awhile."

Brill glanced over at her. She studied his clean-shaven face and short preppy haircut that contrasted with cut off cargo pants and tourist trap tee shirt under the poncho. He holds a blanket tightly in one arm, the shoulder bunched and stiff.

Ron dropped the van in gear and turned the radio volume down by two.

"Where you going?"

"North."

She nodded.

"That's the direction I'm going. Feel like talking or wanna ride?"

He leaned against the door and grimaced.

"You mind?"

"So long as you don't care about my singing."

She reached out, cranked the radio and belted out off key rock and roll.

15

8

CHAPTER EIGHT

An original Matisse adorned one wall of the office on the fiftieth floor. There were windows on two walls that looked out over the city and the Sea beyond. The water below was an emerald shade of green close to the shore that deepened to a blue hue as it went into deeper water.

The desk faced one row of floor to ceiling windows.

It was monochromatic and industrial.

The woman behind it was five seven, trim and muscled. Her hair was meticulously coiffed to highlight strong cheekbones and a delicate neckline. Her lips were full and right now, pursed in anger. She clenched a phone in a white-knuckle grip.

"You didn't complete your mission?"

"We winged him," said Foster through the phone.

Her eyes flashed in rage and she wanted to slam it against the desk.

"I didn't pay you to warn him. He's on alert now. He'll be impossible to reach."

"Negative," said Foster. "He'll move for Baja. We'll wait for him."

Her voice cultured voice did not sound happy.

"I'm not a gambler. I don't play games of chance."

"We'll finish it."

She rose from behind the desk and move with a leonine grace across the floor to a set of shelves. She zeroed in on small four by six photo frame with two smiling hikers next to a gorgeous mountain vista. It's Maddie and Brill, arms around each other.

"I'm freezing the account until it's complete," said Maddie.

"That's acceptable," said Foster after a moment.

She disconnected the call and set the phone down on the shelf. She picked up the picture and started at it, her eyes lost and misty.

9

CHAPTER NINE

A dark sedan cruised down a dusty jungle road driving on the edge of too fast. Wallace gripped the wheel in one hand as he lazily adjusted their trajectory.

"She happy?"

Foster set the phone down between them in the console.

"Not yet, but she will be."

"I don't like this cleanup work."

"Neither do I. But we should arrive in the next several hours and we'll be ahead of him. We'll make an easy job of it and move on."

Wallace grunted.

They drove up on the bumper of a dusty VW bus chugging along. Wallace whipped out around it and punched the accelerator.

Foster glanced up at the driver as they passed.

Ron looked down and him and smiled while she waved.

He returned a curt two fingers and Wallace rocketed past them up the road.

10

CHAPTER TEN

Ron patted the steering wheel in time with the music. She fidgeted with the radio, the gearshift, her khaki shorts. She glanced over at Brill.

"Are you asleep?"

He was lump under the poncho, head lolled against the VW window.

"Do you partake? Mind if I do?"

She reached up to the sun visor and folded it down. A long thin joint was stuck in a rubber band.

Ron stuck one end in her mouth and flicked a lighter open. Brill sat up.

"Want some?"

He shook his head.

"You sure?"

She held the lit joint out to him, bumped his shoulder. He grimaced and gasped.

"You alright?

"Fine," he said.

"You don't look fine. No way, you don't look good at all."

She blew smoke out and it filled the bus like fog. He cracked his window.

"I'll live."

She gave him the once over, twice.

"Are you one of those "macho adventure guys?"

"Not that I'm aware of."

"Where are you going?"

"I thought we were going to ride."

She shrugged and took another hit.

"Makes the time go by. You're the first person I've talked to in five days. I was on a Relic dig. Quixtapa."

Brill shifted around trying to find a more comfortable position.

"Anything interesting?"

"Hieroglyphs we can't decipher. What about you?"

"Vagabonding."

"That's cool. I did that in Thailand for a while. Particular destination?

"Small place in Baja. How far are you going?"

"It's your lucky day. I'm going to San Diego. Keep your cool and you can stay all the way."

Brill held up his hand and showed her an empty palm.

"I'm ice cold," he said.

"There's water in the canteen."

She nodded to the back of the bus. Brill took a deep breath and twisted around to reach for it. His shirt fell open to reveal a blood-soaked tee underneath.

"Oh my God, you're bleeding."

She pulled the van off to the side of the road.

"I'm fine," he grunted.

"You look fine," she said. The sarcasm wasn't lost on him.

"It's a flesh wound–

She tried to move his arm to examine the wound.

"Come back here and fight like a man? Let me see."

"I said I'm fine.

"I know first aid. Let me look."

He pulled away, and leaned against the door.

"I'll be okay."

She watched him a moment, her eyes calculating. He was pale, but breathing steady. Pain etched lines on his face, and he held his body rock still.

"Your funeral," she said.

She dropped the van in gear and pulled back on the road. Ron watched him from the corner of her eyes. He licked his lips and grimaced again.

She reached back and fished up the canteen to pass to him.

"You're going to get an infection.

He took the canteen, unscrewed the top and guzzled a long slow sip.

"Thank you.

"Let me examine it. I'll clean it up, stop the bleeding.

He rested his head against the window again.

"It's fine. Really."

She didn't believe him.

By the look on his face, he didn't believe himself either.

11

CHAPTER ELEVEN

Foster pulled a pistol out of a shoulder holster and began cleaning it with a handkerchief. Wallace concentrated on the road, one hand casually draped across the wheel.

"I don't know why you got in this business. It's never pretty."

Wallace shrugged.

"It's not so bad."

"It's crap. But it's good money crap. I don't know if that justifies it. There are certain rules we follow," said Foster.

"Did you know that? I bet you never would have guessed we have rules. You want to know what the number one rule is? Never tell anyone who you are."

"What happens when you break it?"

"You expose yourself to a certain level of risk."

"What kind of level?"

"The unacceptable kind."

"So, trust no one," said Wallace.

"Exactly."

"Even you?"

"Especially me."

Wallace pondered that for a moment as they drove.

"What about this guy? Do you know who he is?" he asked after a moment.

"Yes."

"Did you bring him in?"

Foster shifted in his seat and sighted down the pistol as he aimed out of the window.

"I found him in Zaire, during the overthrow. He told me he was in the Peace Corps before that."

"Peace Corp training isn't what I thought it would be.

"He was with the Recce. They think he's dead."

He stared through the window at the countryside that slide by inches through the glass and thought back to a different jungle.

12

CHAPTER TWELVE

A jungle stream cut through the thick vegetation. Clear water trickled and tumbled over the rocky bottom, moss covered rocks lined the edge. The stream was penned in by high jagged cliffs, gashed with shadows. There is something about the jungle, any jungle that sets a man's nerve on edge. Call it a primal memory, but the dark shadows and breeze rustled leaves speaks to the lizard brain and calls out a time when man was prey, hunted by apex predators.

Man had fought hard to wallow out of the lizard brain or at least control the response to it.

One of those men detached from the edge of the stream bank, an apex predator in his own right. He is covered with jungle foliage, face painted to match the ground, an H&K G3 gripped tightly in his hands. He carefully picked his way across the rocks and moved upstream.

Two other soldiers similarly clad and armed appeared in the stream behind him and followed, and then another two.

Five members of a six-man Recce squad sneaked up the stream.

They were on a man hunter mission, tasked with recovering a high value target that had been taken by rebel forces, with assistance from Chinese or Russian nationals. Part of their job was to determine who the rebels were working with on this mission, and eliminate that pipeline.

The sixth man was further back. He kept close to the edge of the stream bank as he let the ferns and low hanging branches slip over his utility vest and backpack. He moved slowly, gun pressed to his shoulder. His eyes roamed all over the jungle, his teammates in front of him, the opposite bank. He was keyed up, they all were. Their movements were tense, slow and controlled.

Brill reached a rock and slipped down in the water. His job was to provide cover fire and keep a sight line on the shadowed defiles that scarred both sides of the stream. It was a great site for an ambush and the men knew it.

They also knew the men they were hunting were aware of it too.

Sanders was on point. He reached a fallen log that stretched across the stream and held up a meaty fist. His teammates faded to the edges of the stream but didn't hide against the banks. He stepped over the log, straddled it.

Eight figures popped out of the cliffs, four on each side. They opened fire in short controlled bursts. It was a bloodbath.

The rebels had been coached. Under normal conditions, rebel fighters relied on a spray and pray method in a firefight, meaning they depressed the trigger and kept going until the magazine emptied. They screamed to ancestor gods, God or Allah to help make their aim fly true, but none of the deities accounted for blow back which caused the barrels of their rifles to rise. All Recce's learned to duck as soon as you heard a bullet, or even a buzzing insect by your ear which could denote a bullet, because the Rebels would almost always fire over your head as the barrel lifted.

It allowed a few seconds to take aim and fire, and after thousands of hours at the range, a few seconds was all these operators needed.

These were not normal conditions.

The rebels fired in short controlled bursts from high ground and decimated the scouting team. Bodies flopped into the stream and floated up against the fallen log. They didn't even get a chance to fire back.

Rage washed over Brill. He raised his rifle and prepared to charge. But waited. Something held him back. Perhaps it was the silence of the jungle or the chattering laughter of the eight rebel soldiers as they slid down the embankment and started to pilfer the bodies.

Brill drew a breath in through is nose, slowly blew it out of his mouth. He lined up on the first rebels head, and inched his rifle through an arc as he practiced the movement.

He moved back to the first rebel, a tall soldier that looked like a teenager. Brill popped a round through his eye socket. The rifle barked again, seven more times in less than four seconds.

Eight rebel bodies bobbed in the jungle stream.

Brill squatted in the water and waited.

13

CHAPTER THIRTEEN

Foster rooted underneath the passenger seat and released a Stanley thermos. He unscrewed the top and poured a small cup of cafe con leche. He sniffed the steam and sipped the hot liquid slowly.

"He waited until dark, checked the radio. It was shot, ruined. He went to the extraction point– they never showed up."

"They never found his team?"

"The Russians had a man on the inside of command. Worked with the rebels and the Recce logistics."

"A double payday."

"He didn't get a chance to spend it."

"Brill found him," said Foster grimly.

"That's why he became a killer? Cause no one came to pick him up"

"What's your excuse?"

"I am a material girl and it is a material world."

"That was a song, right? Long time ago?"

"I was trying to keep it to your time line."

"Thanks for that," said Foster.

"So how did you find him?"

"The same way I found you."

"I found you."

"Exactly. In our line of work, it's rather difficult to walk up to someone and just ask."

14

CHAPTER FOURTEEN

Ron watched Brill from the corner of her eye as they bounced along the jungle road.

"I can tell you're not asleep you know," she teased. "Your eyes aren't moving."

"I'm resting," he said.

"Wake up and talk to me. You pretending to sleep is making me sleepy and I need to stay up. Help keep me awake."

"I'll practice my listening skills."

"My name is Veronica. My friends call me Ron. What's your name?"

"Bob. I'm Bob."

"Hi Bob, glad to meet you. Bob. Is that short for Robert?"

"Just Bob."

"Parents a little short on imagination when it comes to names, huh? No worries. I'm sure they had other attributes. Did you get your conversational skills from them?"

"From my grandfather. It's an inherited trait, skips a generation."

"Ha!" she laughed and slapped him on the shoulder.

15

CHAPTER FIFTEEN

Wallace furrowed his brow and he glared at the road.

"But you made me tell you my name."

"Let's just say I learned my lesson."

"From him?"

"Him and others," said Foster. He poured a second cup of coffee.

"You going to offer me any of that?" asked Wallace.

"I told you to be prepared for the trip."

"Yeah, but I thought we would stop somewhere along the way."

"We will stop "somewhere along the way" as you so eloquently put it. That somewhere will be our destination."

"But I'm hungry."

"Then it is well I am only drinking and not eating."

"I'm thirsty too."

"Forethought is an attribute in our business, and one I recommend you embrace heartily. What would you do if you were in a sniper hole for four days waiting for a kill."

Wallace gripped the wheel with both hands. His knuckles grew white as he gripped the wheel.

"I would plan my approach better than waiting four days," he snapped.

Foster ignored the anger in his voice.

"So how long before he told you his name?" Wallace asked after a moment as he tried to reengage the conversation. He ignored the tantalizing cinnamon smell of coffee that filled the car. His stomach did not and rumbled.

"I don't think he ever has."

"His name's not Winger?"

"We were driving to a meet in Memphis one time, doing an assignment for the Dixie Mafia as they moved drugs up from New Orleans to Chicago. He was driving, and we passed an exit sign that was an exact match for his name. Brilliant Winger."

"That's a pretty big tell."

"I have heard a trace of the South in his voice, but this narrowed the region down. I asked. He did not want to discuss further."

CHAPTER SIXTEEN

Ron kept one eye on the road, one hand on the wheel, and stole glances out of the corner of the other to see if Brill would stir and keep talking.

"What do you do in Mexico?"

"Wander."

"Does wandering pay the bills? How do you eat?"

He sat up with a stifled groan and studied the road for a second. His head swiveled around to the van, the road behind them and back to where they were going.

"Do you always ask this many questions?" he tried a grin on and it felt okay, so he kept it.

"Knowledge is power," she grinned back.

Brill's smile turned cryptic and wistful. She noticed.

"What? Did you remember a joke? I love jokes."

"A friend used to tell me that a lot."

"He must be a smart man."

"One of the best," Brill agreed.

She nodded.

"I know a few of those. The world is full of great people if you know what you're looking for. Speaking of great people, we're close to some friends of mine and I was going to crash with them tonight. There's room for you. They won't mind."

Brill flinched as they hit a pothole in the road.

"I don't want to impose," he sucked in air and gasped.

"They won't mind, really. It's that kind of place. I'll vouch for you. Just don't be an asshole and we're good."

"What if I can't make any promises?" he joked.

She hit another pothole and he gasped again.

"You don't look so good Mr. Wanderer."

"I'm okay," he sighed.

Ron didn't believe him, but they were close to camp.

She decided to save the debate and pulled off the jungle road to a well-worn path.

The jungle pressed in on the small van. She bumped along for a hundred yards or so, and Brill cringed with each pothole. He gasped for breath, but kept a stoic look on his face.

Ron pulled the van into a semi-circle of camper buses and RV's pulled around a cleared communal area with a fire pit and tables set up under tarps. It looked like a hippie commune transplanted to the middle of the jungle, with long haired granola people being busy with plants, cooking and the general upkeep of camp life in the jungle.

Brill took it all in through slit eyes.

Even the sentries on top of a couple of the campers who stared out at the jungle with AR-15's and AK-47's held loosely at hand.

"Home sweet home," Ron called.

"You live here?" he wheezed.

"Once upon a time," she answered.

17

CHAPTER SEVENTEEN

They slid into a stop in front of a tiger striped old school bus from the 70's that had been converted into a camper. Brill noted the men on top of the vehicles as they turned their way, not quite lifting their rifles, but wary just the same.

Ron hopped of the driver's side the van and greeted three people who spilled out of the bus. They wrapped up in a group hug, a tangle of arms and hair and smiles.

Brill got flashes of the newcomers. They didn't look like hippies. They were young, grad students maybe, or of that age where idealism met revolutionary fervor and planted the seeds of hope for a change. He had been there once, long ago. They wore khaki fatigues, most likely second hand from surplus shops or else shipped down by parents or friends from the United States. The clothing was used, but not well worn, which meant it had never seen any real action, just traveled from a Quartermaster Corps somewhere and ended up in the jungle.

"Amigos!" he heard Ron shout. "Mi familia."

She broke away and hugged each in turn starting with Scooter. Brill dismissed him on sight. He was lean to the point of emaciation, with long stringy hair and a scraggly beard. He tugged at his hair and put the end in his mouth to suck on as he stared through small round glasses he felt gave him an intellectual air.

"We wondered where you were," he said in a nasally voice.

"Hung up an Quixtapa."

"We missed you," said Dana, a solid squat red head with Irish green eyes and linebacker shoulders.

"Are you staying?"

"Just for the night," said Ron. "I've got a deadline in San Diego."

"Stay longer than a night," Scooter pleaded.

"Can't hermano. I wish I could."

The third was Enrique, a handsome man with a face that hinted of Spanish heritage.

"What did you bring us?"

"A wanderer like me," she answered. "He's banged up, bleeding. He won't let me look at it though."

Dana's face morphed over to that of a concerned mother. She gazed through the windshield at Brill with soft eyes.

"Want me to talk to him?"

Brill opened the door and they watched him as he pulled himself out of the passenger seat and held himself up by the door. He sucked in a breath, and stepped toward the group.

Scooter extended a sweaty palm.

"You are staying with us tonight too, brother?"

Brill reached out for the hand but missed. He was surprised. Normally he was pretty good at handshakes, as simple as they were. And standing. He had years of practice with that. Standing was easy. Just keep your feet apart and braced and balance. So why was it so hard right now, and how was it getting dark so fast?

He missed the hand and fell to the earth hard.

18

CHAPTER EIGHTEEN

The key to waking up in a strange room is to try and maintain the pretense of sleep and allow a moment to acclimate. Brill didn't flick open his eyes, or try to jump out of bed or call out. None of the things people do in movies, even though it would seem to be a normal reaction.

He became aware of sounds first, coming to him from down a long tunnel. They were muffled voices. He controlled his breathing, and slit open his eyes and tried not to squint at the light.

The room was gray, with a window that stared out at a brick wall. The steady beep of a heart monitor matched the rush of blood in his ears. The murmurs came from the corner, so he turned his head and cracked one eye open just a little.

Foster spoke with a blood-stained surgeon. The doctor was Turkish, a bushy mustache bounced as he explained something to Foster. His scrubs and gown were covered with blood.

They both noticed his head move. Foster looked like he hadn't slept for days, his normally meticulous suit was rumpled, bags under his sunken eyes.

"Can you hear me?"

He nodded. The voice still sounded muffled, but overpowered the rush of blood in his pounding head.

"Did I get the mark?" he whispered.

He must have said it softly, but Foster still put a hand on the butt of a pistol under his arm and glanced at the doctor.

The man hadn't heard.

"It's better we discuss that later," said Foster. "You gave us a scare."

Brill moved his head back painfully and glanced down at his body. He wiggled the fingers on his right hand and felt them, all five, and did the same for his left hand and then ten toes.

All was accounted for and all ached. Foster probably had them ease up on the morphine just so he wouldn't let a nugget of information slip. His body was wrapped up like the mummy, the bandages tight against his skin. Skin that ached just as bad as his muscles.

"Well Doctor?" asked Foster picking up the conversation Brill interrupted with a shift of his head.

"He will recover, I think. We are through the worst of it now. Let us see how he is after some rest."

The doctor hurried out of the room, his mind already on the next patient he had to visit.

"Success?" asked Brill now that they were alone.

"They sent in a kamikaze. What do you remember?"

Brill shook his head, but it hurt too much to move far. Just a micro movement really, a fraction of an inch to the left, a fraction of an inch to the right.

"You got the mark," Foster answered. He placed a hand on

Brill's shoulder. "Get some rest and I'll be back later."

19

CHAPTER NINETEEN

The world looks different viewed through cross hairs. It's an extreme example of tunnel vision. A good sniper is taught the power of focus, a great sniper combines speed with precision.

Brill leaned against of row of boxes five feet back from a window that looked out over a set of row houses in Ireland.

The day was gray and cloudy, threatened rain that had yet to fall.

He's comfortable in jeans and a canvas work coat, looking like every other blue-collar worker that populated the street below. A couple of young kids played and yelled as they batted around a worn soccer ball.

He settled the stock against his shoulder and watched the world through scope, his breath low and controlled.

A British Army Transport paused in the street to let the kids clear out before it rumbled past. They yelled and flipped off the soldiers.

The radio headset in his ear crackled.

"Shadowboxer?"

"Go," he said.

"They're breaking up."

"Confirmed. Now go."

He shifted the barrel of the rifle to a short stout young man standing on the corner. He's dressed in jeans and a jacket that looked a lot like what he was wearing. The man started walking away from the building and just before he turned the corner, he glanced up at the half open window where Brill was hiding.

"Damn it," Brill sighed.

He pulled a silenced pistol from his pocket and placed it on a box in front of him.

"Spotter," he said into the radio.

"Yeah? Go."

"You just gave me away."

"No one noticed. I swear," the man said nervously. "Abort?"

Brill studied the street. The kids still played. Walkers walked. Everything looked the exact same. Maybe he had gotten lucky.

"Sir?" the Spotter asked again.

"Negative. Proceed to pick up."

He continued the mission.

The Spotter walked ten yards up the street and passed an alley way. Two goons jumped him and dragged him through the trash and behind a dumpster. The taller one, Danny pulled a pistol from his jacket and shot the young man in the back of the head.

Frankie gagged.

"For Fuck's sake man, you could have let me step back."

He wiped blood spatter off his face and hands.

Danny grabbed him by the collar and pulled him close.

"You make sure I'm good and gone before you pull, you bugger."

Frankie pulled a block of C4 out of his jacket pocket and shoved a detonator into the clay like lump.

"Relax Dan-O," he smiled. He was missing several teeth in his freckle faced grin. "I'm a professional."

"Aya, you're a whiz, all right. If I'm gonna die, this ain't how it should happen."

"Just move your arse, ya shit. We're outta time."

Danny nodded and walked around the corner. He stuffed the pistol into his coat pocket and ducked his head down around the shoulders to disguise himself further. He hunched and tried to limp to hide his gait.

Brill noticed the young man dressed like a dock worker limping home after a morning shift. The scope followed him for ten steps and dismissed him as a threat. Just another lad on the streets of Belfast looking for a pint.

The door up the street opened and he swung the barrel of his rifle to the shadows inside.

A black Mercedes turned onto the street and rolled to a stop in front of the steps. The kids playing soccer vacated the road quickly and ran around the corner. A second car pulled behind the first and parked. Six large bodyguards exited the car and created a wall from the passenger door up the steps with three men on each side.

Brill moved the scope sight to the car door. It opened quickly, and three men hustled out. They all looked similar, same height, same haircut but each had on a different color suit, black, blue and gray. Each of them carried a leather attaché case.

That confirmed it for Brill. He set the scope on blue suit and pulled the trigger. A hole opened in his forehead and he jerked back, tossed the attaché case up into the air. It blocked the second shot from hitting gray suit. A bodyguard tackled the man and took two in the back of the head that puffed out a pink mist as they fell.

The bodyguards opened on the building across the street. No one had heard the shots, and they couldn't tell where the shooter was, so they fell back on the old reliable standard of spray and pray. The street bounced gunfire off the buildings.

Bullets shattered the window and showered glass across Brill. He jumped up, kicked out the shutters and popped the five bodyguards and black suit with fast precise shots.

Gray suit crawled out from under the dead weight of the man on top of him. He scrambled for the door of the car and what he hoped was safety inside.

Brill drew a bead on his head and pulled the trigger.

A noise at the door behind him made him spin. He peppered the wall with shots at just above waste level, stitched a line as someone ran down the hall. They screamed when he hit them.

"Not yet! Not yet!"

Brill dove behind the box at the window. The building erupted around him in an explosion of dust and debris. The front end of the wall collapsed and spilled three floors out onto the street in a pile of bricks and detritus.

Danny ran around the corner and began picking through the rubble. He lifted Frankie's dead body and hefted it over his shoulder. He stumbled away as a dust covered hand pushes aside a section of broken brick with the tip of a silenced pistol. The hand flopped down.

A silver Peugeot slid to a stop by the collapsed building and Foster jumped out. He ripped bricks and broken bits of building to the side and grabbed Brill. He jerked him out of the rubble and folded him into the backseat of the car as sirens wailed closing

45

in.

20

CHAPTER TWENTY

A cloud of gray slowly coalesced into focus as the rim of a glass held by a slender hand. The hand was on a muscular arm that led straight of the shoulder next to a smile. A beautiful smile with white teeth and the hint of a dimple. It was a nice smile, the kind that was used to getting what she wanted, and wielded like a weapon.

"Drink this," she said.

He sniffed the rim. Water, which technically had no smell and was telling in and of itself. Besides, he reasoned, what other clear liquid would a sick man get? It had a probability of being water. Unless he was in Russia or Russian hands. Russians thought vodka was a magical elixir designed by the gods of the steppe as a cure all.

He sipped at the edge of the cup and was right. Just water. The tinge in his shoulder made him crave a little vodka though, if just to numb the ache.

He took a larger gulp and she pulled the cup away.

"I'll give you more in a minute," she chided. "We were worried. Do you know how much blood you lost?"

"Three gallons?"

"Funny. Good to see your sense of humor didn't leak out all over my van floor. Do you know how long I'm going to have to scrub to get out the stains?"

"Surprised you could see it under all the junk on the floor," he groaned.

"Jokes huh? Still got jokes. I think that's a good sign."

"Where are we?" he asked and looked around.

The walls bent in at the top of the narrow eight-foot-wide space. Sheer curtains covered rows of windows near the intersection of wall and ceiling.

"Still at the camp," she told him, and it clicked.

He was in the bus or a bus, but which one he couldn't be sure. It was a rudimentary hospital suite, so perhaps these rebels, if he could call them that, or anthropology students pretending at rebellion had seen an action or two. One side had the cot he was on against a wall, and the other was a series of plastic bins with drawers, the opaque plastic hinting at the medical supplies inside.

Ron rolled the sheet down from his chest. It's a map work of scars, intricate and delicate, some tiny, some larger.

Scars tell a story, or most stories, the good ones at least, end with a scar or two as a memento and reminder of a lesson learned.

His chest told of a story that lessons had been harsh. It was yet to be determined what he had learned.

"What happened to you?"

"Wrong place, wrong time," he answered.

"More than one wrong place."

"More than one wrong time."

"Did you learn your lesson?"

He licked his lips and indicated he wanted more water. She held the glass to his mouth for a sip, then another and pulled it away. She set the glass down and lifted a flattened bullet.

"Who shot you?

The bus sagged as someone stepped on board.

The mosquito netting that separated them from the front compartment moved aside and Enrique stood there.

"Is he dead?"

"You heard us talking," she said. "Not yet."

Enrique moved and stood behind Ron. He stared down at the mishmash of scars and tried to hide a wince. He failed.

"How you feel amigo?"

"Thirsty," Ron answered for Brill.

"Some of those look pretty old," the rebel nodded toward his chest.

"Enrique-" warned Ron.

"And some not so old, I think."

"Enrique," she said again and this time it sounded like a command. He took a step back.

"What?" he grumbled. "I can't ask a question?"

"He is a guest," she stared him down with icy eyes. "We treat him like any other."

Enrique shook his head and pointed.

"With a pattern like that, he could be a mole."

The bus sagged again, and Dana skittered on board. She flitted to the end of the bus.

"Who's a mole?" she asked in her high-pitched voice.

"No one is a mole," said Ron.

"We haven't established that yet," said Enrique.

Dana saw the mess of Brill's chest and yanked a camp stool over to sit next to him.

"Oh my God," her voice trembled. "Who did this to you?"

Tears gathered in the corner of her eyes as she traced the tip of a rough finger across the network of tissue. Her lip quivered.

"They got me too, you know."

She unbuttoned her shirt and opened it up to reach the plain white tee she wore under. She lifted the tee and revealed scars across her side and lower back.

"They had me for six months," she said. "Whipped me. And other things."

She dropped her shirt and put her hands on his chest. Her haunted eyes stared into his as she tried to offer comfort.

"How long did they have you?"

"They may still have him," Enrique snapped.

He reached down and gently pulled Dana back from the cot.

"No one has me," Brill answered.

He struggled to sit up, but Ron pushed him back with one hand.

"Who shot you?"

"I told you. Wrong place."

"Wrong time," she finished for him and held up his pistol.

His eyes narrowed as he watched her closely.

"This is a Company issued silence," she said.

"What company?"

She twirled the gun on the end of her finger.

"And none of us can guess who modified the gun. We've never seen anything like it."

"What do archeology students know about guns?" he asked.

"We know who supplies the policia," snarled Enrique. "The same men that gave you this silencer."

"You have to tell us who shot you," said Ron. "Or we'll have to assume a story for you and ours is a worst-case scenario."

Brill glanced from her to the others and back again. She held his gaze, as did Enrique, both itching for a fight maybe.

He was, muscles tense, vein throbbing in his neck, one hand clenched in a fist.

The other hand was on Dana, who looked at him with sympathy and concern, even as she took a half step behind Enrique. Cautious, just in case.

At one hundred percent, he could take them. It would take less than four seconds. But he wasn't one hundred percent. He couldn't even be sure he was fifty percent until he moved, and given the situation, he wasn't sure he should move.

"Talk to us," growled Enrique.

"Talk is overrated," Brill shot back.

Ron passed the pistol to Enrique and stood back from the cot.

"He's not going to tell us who he works for," she said.

"Then that is answer enough."

"I can't do it," she said.

Dana moved between them and stared down at Brill.

"We helped you," she said. "Now you have to help us. Don't make them kill you, please. Are you here to spy on us?"

"I'm not a spy," Brill snorted.

"How do we know?" asked Enrique.

21

CHAPTER TWENTY-ONE

Foster stood in the corner of the roach infested motel room. The carpet was stained with dark blotches from years of abuse, the walls were a Jackson Pollack painting of browns, and mold and gunk. The furniture was third rate, bought second hand from another flop house that was going out of business due to too many murders.

There were two beds though, large, saggy and lumpy and private.

A pay by the hour affair that promised a clerk who paid zero attention to the two men as they checked in, one in the parking lot in the car, and the other wearing glasses into the smoke choked front office.

Foster flipped one of the saggy mattresses against the wall.

"Never point a pistol across the room," he instructed. "It's made for close range work."

Foster moved in front of the mattress by the wall.

"Shoot at my head, once."

Wallace raised an eyebrow. Foster nodded, go on.

His protege reached into his jacket, pulled a pistol out of the shoulder holster, aimed and fired. Foster shifted his head left. The bullet puffed into the mattress with an explosion of feathers and a dull thud.

Wallace stared at him, dumbfounded.

"If you can't surprise a mark, he can move out of the way. Success in our business can be measured in centimeters."

"How did you do that?"

"I watched your finger. The knuckle goes white as the muscles contract. A trigger takes less than a pound of pressure, but there is a tell you're always on the watch for."

Foster pulled his pistol from the holster and aimed it at Wallace.

"Allow me to demonstrate," he pulled the trigger.

Wallace threw himself across the bed as the pistol dry fired.

"Holy shit, you almost shot me."

"Observe," Foster said in a cool calm voice.

He aimed the pistol at Wallace's face again. The firing pin clicked and clicked and clicked as he showed the younger man how to watch the finger change color.

22

CHAPTER TWENTY-TWO

The tip of his finger turned purple and the knuckle shifted over to white. Brill jerked his head to one side as Enrique pulled the trigger. A puff of feathers erupted out of the pillow.

Brill kicked Enrique's hand against the wall, jackknifed out of bed and grabbed his arm. He twisted Enrique's wrist and popped the gun loose. He spun the rebel around and slammed him into the side of the bus, caught the pistol and crammed it into his neck.

"I told you I'm not a spy," he coughed.

He winced and slumped against the bed, but held the guns steady. Enrique pulled himself up, massaged his throat, massaged his arm, his hand moved back and forth as he tried to make up his mind which hurt worse. Neither injury burned more than his pride though.

"Damn," whispered Dana. "You pulled some stitches."

Brill felt the syrupy stickiness of blood as it oozed down the back of his shoulder and arm.

Dana grabbed the gauze.

"May I?"

He nodded and leaned the injured shoulder toward her.

"How did you do that?" Ron asked from two steps away. The confines of the bus were tight, but she still managed to wedge herself closer to the door.

"Practice," hissed Brill as Dana pressed on the pucker wound. "Lots of practice."

"I don't trust him," Enrique groaned.

"You shouldn't," said Brill. "But you're not going to kill me for it."

23

CHAPTER TWENTY-THREE

Snow melt turned the rocky trail into a muddy slog up the side of the mountains. The path was overgrown, hardly used, but the two hikers didn't seem to care. They laughed and giggled as they picked their away upwards.

A majestic landscape surrounded them as they stopped to take in the view. Snowcapped peaks hovered in the distance, higher than their elevation, and Aspen woods stretched across a wavering tree line just below them.

They could have kept going higher, if they had the proper gear. Above them the path veered to the left and twisted around the Western edge of the mountain they climbed. A spring bubbled from somewhere further up, a trickle that carved through the rock to grow bolder and larger below.

They stopped at the stream at a crevice. Here it was wider than six feet, too hard to jump. The melting snow and ice had turned the trickle into a steady flow.

"I don't want to get my feet wet," she said.

Brill sat on a rock and pulled off his boots and socks.

"Hop on."

"I don't know if I can trust you."

He smiled over his shoulder at her and took a step out into the water.

"You probably shouldn't," his grin was infectious. "It's cold. I can't wait forever."

"What if you drop me?" she teased.

"I promise."

He winked, his smirk promising that he might.

She laughed and shook her head.

"Take a chance," he shivered.

That did it. She took two quick steps and launched herself at his back. He staggered, not because of the weight but the speed with which she latched on.

He recovered and carried her across the stream in a few quick steps.

"No worries, right?" he said as he set her upright and put his wool socks and hiking boots back on.

She bent down, grabbed his face and kissed him long and deep. It was a good kiss, full of potential and promises. He didn't want her to pull back, but she finally did.

"I always worry," she smiled.

She continued slogging up the mud trail. He tied off his boots and marched after her.

24

CHAPTER TWENTY-FOUR

They saw the steam before they wandered over the crest. It made a fine layer of fog that drifted across the ground and floated down the trail. The hot spring was a geothermal event where the stream intersected a vent in the rocks. The stream created a series of pools that cascaded down the rocks.

Brill sat on a rock and slipped out of his hiking boots again. He began to strip his jeans.

"Get in," Maddie laughed. "Wait for me."

He slid over the edge of a rock and eased down into the scalding water.

"Where are you going?"

She slung her pack over one shoulder and traipsed down the path.

"Little girl's business."

She disappeared through the trees. He watched her go as he relaxed into the water.

25

CHAPTER TWENTY-FIVE

Maddie glanced over her shoulder when she hit the trial. Brill was up to his neck in the pool, eyes closed as he lounged. She shifted up on her toes and sprinted through the woods, trees whizzing by in a snow-covered blur.

She spied the ridge off to the side and darted between two evergreens to angle up the edge. She reached the precipice and threw herself down on the ground as she slung her pack in front of her.

She whipped out a monocular and peered through it. A pristine slope slid into view.

She laid the monocular down and began to assemble a rifle from her pack. She slid the barrel into the stock and locked it down, twisted a shoulder mount into the stock and set it against her shoulder to lock it. She glided a scope onto the slide and tightened it on pre-determined marks.

Then she peered through the scope, tracking the edge of the slope in the distance.

A figure topped the slope and whisked down in a spray of snow. It was followed by another skier, both in bright pastel colors that were requirements in the back country. It would be easier to pick out a body against the snowy white backdrop in case there was an accident.

Maddie tracked the first skier in his powder blue jacket. She noted the pattern he was cutting, a four-count breath as he held a line, one, two three, four, turn and then again.

She confirmed the count with two more twists in the snow, then counted down with him as she watched through the scope. Her finger tightened on the trigger.

The skier turned, and she pulled. Poof.

He sprawled in the snow and kept sliding.

She sent another shot through the bobbing head as it bounced across the snow pack.

Maddie rolled away from the ridge and grabbed her pack. She sprinted back down the trail, disassembling the rifle as she ran and tossing parts into the woods off the path.

She skidded to a halt just before the break in the trees around the pool and seductively swaggered toward the pool.

"Did you miss me?" she smiled at Brill.

Her fingers unzipped her jacket and let it fall. They moved to her shirt and pants as she left a trail of clothes to the rocks and slid in beside him.

"Excruciatingly," he sighed as he wrapped his arms around her and pulled her close.

26

CHAPTER TWENTY-SIX

Brill crawled out of the hiker's tent and stretched. The sun had yet to crest the mountain behind them, but light filtered through the shallow valley next to the steaming springs.

"Coffee," said Maddie as she stood next to him and wrapped her arms around his waist.

"I packed a French Press," he answered. "Put on a kettle while I pack our gear."

They broke camp as they boiled water and made two steaming cups of coffee which they sipped while sunlight dripped over the ridge and washed through the trees.

"Did you enjoy yourself?" she asked.

He reached for her hand.

"We should take more trips like this," she continued.

"Plan it," he winked.

They rinsed out the cups, packed up and hiked down the trail. A mile later he stopped and raised a hand.

"What?"

He raised a finger to his nose, and drew her off the trail.

Footsteps marched up the steep trail toward them. Three Austrian soldiers slogged up the trail, rifles held in their hands.

"It's just soldiers," she said and stepped back on the trail.

The three men stopped. They didn't raise their rifles, but tension lined their faces. The leader of the group was Hans, the man on point. His face was young, barely out of his teens and he licked his lips in a nervous habit.

"Papieres, bitte," he asked.

Maddie reached into her pocket and pulled out her passport while nodding to Brill.

"They want our papers."

Brill handed his documents over.

"What are you doing here?" Hans continued in German.

"We found the hot spring and spent the night," she answered flawlessly.

She cuddled her arm through Brill's and pulled him close. He watched the exchange with alert eyes.

"It is not permitted to sleep the night."

"Who said we slept," she answered.

The two young soldiers behind Hans snorted and giggled.

"Have you seen any others?" asked Hans as he handed their papers back.

"We haven't."

Hans studied Brill for a moment and something made the hairs on his neck stand up.

"Do you speak German?" he asked.

Brill shook his head. Hans watched them both for a moment, but they looked like a young couple in love out for a hike.

"No more nights here," he warned.

Maddie flashed a brilliant smile.

"Thank you," she said.

She led Brill further down the trail. The soldier's continued the climb up.

"What was that about?" Brill asked, glancing over his shoulder to watch the three young men disappear over the ridge.

"I have no idea," she shrugged.

27

CHAPTER TWENTY-SEVEN

Tourists descend on every part of Paris like schools of piranha in a feeding frenzy. The West Bank held a special place in their hearts with echoes of Hemingway and Fitzgerald sounding in the shadows. Artists followed, young people hoping some of the magic in the atmosphere would somehow leech through their skin. They competed with tourists for space in the small cafe's and sidewalk bistros during the day and evening.

Morning was the best time for locals or the few Parisian visitors in the know. Before the buses vomited visitors onto the cobblestone streets, before the hotels stopped serving warm croissants and giant mugs of au lait.

Brill sat on one side of a small table and stared at the outline of Notre Dame. Foster was across from him, a delicate cup near his hand.

"Are you going to tell her?" he asked.

He studied Brill carefully.

"Would you?"

Foster smiled and took a sip, careful not to spill any coffee onto his white pinpoint cotton shirt.

"I'm not the man to ask son. I'm working on wife number three."

"Do any of them know?"

"As far as the world knows, I manage investments."

Foster waved one finger over for the waiter to bring a refill.

"Not bad work, if you can get it."

"She might not understand. It's not like I'm saving the world."

Foster nodded.

The thing about working with a man in this line of work for more than a year, you get to know them.

When he found Brill in Africa, the boy was a stone. He had all the skills, he had the requisite brutality, and he had killed before, many times. It was in his eyes.

Foster was the sculptor, taking tool to rock and chipping away everything that was unnecessary to make a work of art.

No, they didn't save the world in the usual fashion. There were no capes, no treaties, no daring heroics into burning buildings. He couldn't even lie to himself about what they did.

They killed people for money. He tried to steer them toward killing the right people, but a moral compass could point in any direction for enough cash. He didn't even bother to try and fool himself with any other platitude.

"No, we don't save the world," he sighed.

The two men smiled at each other across the table and said at the same time.

"Pays great though."

Brill perked up and Foster felt his pulse quicken. The man sitting across from him was a predator and scented prey. He pulled a few Euro's out of his pocket and set them on the table.

"My treat," he said as he stood.

He took a large overcoat from the other chair and draped it across his arm. He reached into a shoulder holster and pulled a silenced pistol out, hid it under the coat.

"Don't tell her. We live in a different world, you and me."

Foster turned, and as he turned he pulled the trigger twice.

Across the street, a rotund man with a wispy blond woman on his arm pitched forward and collapsed. The woman screamed as the man leaked blood on the cobblestones.

Brill jumped up with the crowd.

It was easy to tell the heroic hearts from the sheep. People ran in two directions, some for cover and away from the noise. Others ran to aid the fallen man.

"You may be right," Brill said.

"You'll see," Foster answered.

Brill moved with the crowd in one direction while Foster slipped away in the other.

There would be no tourists on this street today.

CHAPTER TWENTY-EIGHT

The Ballroom was packed with beautiful people in Armani suits and couture gowns. They spun around the small dance floor in front of a tuxedo clad orchestra led by a small man bouncing a baton and smiling over his shoulder at the swirling couples.

The room was dark, pools of spotlight casting harsh shadows, the tables lit by candles and wall sconces dimmed to pinpricks.

Brill marched through the crowd, eyes scanning as he moved. He slid between the tables and couples, avoided contact as he moved like a predator through the herd.

He caught sight of something in his periphery and paused as he glanced over. There was Maddie, leaning across a table and laughing softly into the ear of a man in a white tuxedo jacket.

Brill turned and angled toward the bar as he tried to stay out of her line of sight. She turned away from the table and he rolled into the bar. He could see her in the reflection of a small mirror set above the glassware.

A young pretty bartender hurried down to him.

"What can I get you?"

"Bourbon," said Brill, his eyes locked on the mirror. "Three fingers."

She poured the drink and slid it to him. He held the glass to his lips but didn't sip.

Maddie moved to the next table, put her hand on the shoulder of the man and bent down to whisper to the woman. Brill caught sight of another man moving through the crowd. He is impeccably dressed, with a rim of silver gray hair and groomed beard.

Brill watched the man reach his table and grab a well-endowed young woman by the arm. When he jerked her out of her seat, there was almost a show as everything rolled around and threatened to spill from her top.

She glared at the man, but he ignored her.

Brill swallowed down his drink and set the glass on top of the bar with a twenty-dollar bill underneath.

He glanced at Maddie, waited for her back to turn, then pushed through the crowd again. He made the foyer before the bearded man and the girl.

He leaped across the counter into the coat check room, and spun as he landed.

"Take a break," he said to the coat check girl.

"You're not supposed to be back here," she warned as she backed away.

"I slipped," said Brill.

"I'm getting the manager," she shouted.

Brill held a finger to his lips. She fumbled for the doorknob and tried to yank it open. He stubbed it closed with the toe of his polished shoe and grabbed her wrist. Twisting gently, he directed her to the floor.

"Sorry about that," he whispered as the Bearded man walked up with a haughty air.

"Get in the car," he slurred to his companion and shoved her toward the door. He tossed a claim ticket down on the counter and glared at Brill with bleary eyes.

"I'm in a hurry."

Brill reached for the ticket as the Bearded man turned his head to watch the girl leave. Brill kept reaching until he grabbed his lapel and yanked him across the counter top.

He dragged the man into the coat room and pressed a silenced H&K into his chest. The man landed with a plop and Brill thudded two slugs into his chest.

He vaulted over the counter and walked through the door.

As it closed behind him, he heard the gurgling scream of the coat check girl echo through the foyer. It sounded just like a woman with a dead man's head in her lap.

29

CHAPTER TWENTY-NINE

A standoff is pretty standard in the world of espionage and it usually ends with both parties backing off or backing down. If every encounter ended with a shootout, there wouldn't be anyone left alive, or worse create a series of cascading grudges and revenge hits.

There are two ways to react in any standoff situation. Hold your ground until the other guy blinks, then magnanimously allow everyone to holster their weapons and get down to business. Or wait for a distraction and take full advantage.

Brill preferred the distraction method.

The bus tilted slightly as Scooter stepped on board.

"How is he up?" he called from the front of the bus. He fumbled with the AK-47 strap, struggled to bring it to bear.

Brill drew and shot the rifle out of his hands. Scooter yelped and held both hands high above his head.

"Holy crap man!" he screamed.

"What is it with you people!" Brill shouted at him.

He waved everyone back with his gun. Blood leaked from his shoulder as he moved, and he leaned against the bed trying to stay up. Ron showed him her hands, palms out as she stepped closer.

"Who are you dude?" she said in a soft voice. "I mean, if you're not a spy for the Federales, you have to be a mole for the US. You shoot like Quick Draw McGraw."

Brill cracked a tiny smile.

"I watched that when I was a kid," he grunted.

"Want to trade secrets?" Ron said as she took one step closer. "We tell you, you tell us?"

Brill glanced at the scarred rifle resting on the bus floor.

"None of my business," he said.

The bus tilted again as another member of the Commune shoved his lanky head into the door.

"Federales!"

Scooter followed him out as the camp exploded in activity, like an ant hill kicked over. People ran around, grabbing weapons and supplies and hightailed it into the jungle bush.

"I told you not to trust him," mumbled Enrique.

Brill stuck his pistol into the waistband of his pants.

"Not mine," he said. "You were followed."

The group of people surrounding him looked anxious to run, but even more afraid he would shoot them in the back if they made any sudden moves. They knew how fast he could draw.

"Move," he commanded. "Move!"

Dana scrambled for the exit, as Ron leaned back to let her pass. Enrique stopped by Brill and growled.

"I won't forget."

"Take it up with you later, Rique," Brill smiled.

Enrique shoved past him and bent to grab the fallen AK.

71

"Leave it," commanded Brill.

Enrique glared as he left the bus and ran into the jungle.

"Are you with them?" Brill asked Ron.

"What are you going to do?"

He checked the clip in his pistol.

"Think I could talk my way past them?"

A half smile played across her luscious lips.

"You don't know where you are."

"I didn't think so."

He bent over to scoop up the AK and collapsed with a groan. Ron grabbed him and helped him sit up.

"You're not so good at the talking," she teased and helped him to his feet. "Are you going to be okay?"

"This? It's just a flesh wound," he said in a fake British accent.

She smiled, and half carried him out of the bus.

Overhead an ancient Huey Helicopter buzzed over the treetops as it circled the clearing. A solider on an M50 leaned out of the open side and raked the jungle with bullets.

Ron stopped and reached for Brill's pistol. He leaned away, raised the AK and shot the helicopter motor. Smoke poured from the engine cowling and the chopper whirled away with a high-pitched whine.

"We need to move," she said and dragged him toward the thick undergrowth.

30

CHAPTER THIRTY

Maddie sat back in her chair with the phone pressed to her ear. She nodded twice.

"I understand," she said into the receiver.

She pulled it away from her ear and slammed it into the phone base so hard it cracked in half. She spun her chair around and stared out of the window.

The skyline was beautiful, a collection of silver skyscrapers that towered over the green verdant landscape. Mountains blurred the horizon and she glared at those in particular, hating the way remembering made her feel.

She slowly turned the chair back to the desk and reached into the drawer. Maddie pulled out a Glock 17, checked the magazine and chamber.

CHAPTER THIRTY-ONE

Foster sat across from Wallace and stared. No matter what anyone said, the man could eat. He had a plate full of two burritos, three tacos and a tamale. He ate like a man who learned chow from the Army, hunched over his plate, each arm in a circle in a protective perimeter. The right arm shoveled, the mouth chewed. At least he kept it closed.

One of the things Foster detested were poor table manners, which were so abundant in the parts of the world where he operated, it made him perpetually queasy. It helped him stay thin.

"You better watch your figure," he warned. "A man in our business has to keep fit."

Wallace shoveled a forkful of burrito into his mouth and chewed methodically. He swallowed and patted his trim stomach.

"I've got a fast metabolism."

"So did I," Foster sighed as he let the man focus on his food.

32

CHAPTER THIRTY-TWO

Brill and Foster stood across from each other in a narrow unlit doorway. The street beyond them was dark thanks to three well placed and silenced shots from Brill's pistol. They wore matching dark overcoats against the chill night air, and to help blend into the grime covered brick of the buildings.

"Do you want to know what they do in there?"

"Does it matter?"

Foster reached under his coat and extracted a backpack. He held it out to Brill by the straps.

"We counted nineteen under an hour ago. No one has came nor went. Want some help?

Brill opened the backpack and pulled out two silenced pistols. He worked the slides and checked the mags. Each was full with one chambered.

"Thirty-two," he said. "No problem."

A truck pulled into the far side of the street, headlights washing across the walls. They ducked further back into the doorway.

Brakes squealed as the truck crunched to a stop in front of a doorway up the street.

Six men climbed out of the truck and shuffled up the stairs. They were dressed in what Foster referred to as gangster leathers, the ubiquitous black leather coat that left them formless and shapeless, enough to cover their weapons.

"Twenty-five," he said.

"Thirty-two," Brill smiled at him.

"Plus, a backup piece?"

"Would you have taught me any different?"

Foster nodded and pulled a pistol out of his pocket. He held one gloved hand over it but kept it free.

"I'm here," he said. "Just in case."

Brill nodded once and jogged across the street to the doorway. Foster lifted a wrist to his mouth and spoke into a hidden microphone.

"Does it work?"

Brill wiggled his jaw and twisted his head to one side to seat the ear piece better.

"You tell me."

"Loud and clear," Foster answered over the ear piece.

Brill pushed through the door and walked down a dark hallway.

"Third floor, last room," said Foster.

Brill hit the stairs and moved up quickly, taking two at a time.

"I'm watching," Foster said from below as he monitored with an infrared monocular. He spied two outlines standing where the stairwell ended on the third-floor hallway.

"Two bodies, top of the stairs," he called out.

Brill pulled the two pistols from his pockets and moved up the last flight of stairs one step at a time. He moved like a lion slowly approaching prey. One of the guards must have heard something and peeked over the railing.

Brill raised the pistol and shot him through the mouth.

The body dropped on the rail and gravity fought to pull it over. Brill rushed the last four steps and hit the hallway at a dead run.

The second guard was running for the last doorway. Brill sent two silenced rounds into his back and watched him thud to the floor.

He approached the door and listened. It was quiet.

He expected to hear talking, the noise of the television, other sounds of a room occupied, but the silence was telling. They heard him, or they had been tipped off.

He leaned around, kicked the door open and ducked back behind the wall. Shots erupted through the open door and peppered the plaster across from him.

In a lull, Brill rolled around the opening and shot once with each pistol. Two men dropped.

Bullets blasted the wall behind him and stitched a pattern above his head, showered him with white dust.

He jerked around the edge of the door frame and dropped the machine gunner and another man. Eleven men shot at him, but he rolled out of sight.

He needed a distraction, but didn't to call up Foster. As if thinking of him summoned the man, he called over the radio.

"Situation."

"Under control."

One of the men grabbed the machine gun and sent an entire magazine through the wall.

"Sounds like it," said Foster.

Brill pulled out his back up piece and tossed it through the door.

77

"Grenade!" he screamed and ran in after it.

All the men in the room saw was a shape soaring through the air and someone yelling grenade. They were military trained, so instinct kicked in. When you hear grenade, you duck.

Even as they ducked they saw a shadow move into the room. Brill shot left and right, each bullet finding a mark.

Four men ran through a side door and kicked it closed. Brill moved to one side of the door and leaned down against the wall.

Foster watched from below as the red bodies in the monocular slowly shifted toward blue.

"Good work," he said. "Five in the next room. They're waiting."

"Thanks," said Brill.

He glanced at one of the dead men, grabbed the body and propped it against the door frame.

He kicked open the door and held the body in place as bullets slammed into it. He shoved the corpse inside and slid under it, shooting as he crawled. Five shots, five men down.

He rolled from under the body and scanned the room with his pistol.

"Uh oh," he breathed.

The room was empty with two sets of thick double doors on opposite walls. Brill makes a complete circle from one door to the other.

"What is uh oh?" asked Foster.

"What do you see," Brill took a step back toward the door.

"I have nothing."

"Find them," Brill shouted.

One of the double doors opened both side and he spun toward it.

Bodies spilled out, shooting. Brill fires back, drops low and runs toward the men pouring into the room. They trip over the first wave of bodies he dropped, but more are behind them.

One pistol clicked dry, he side armed it into one of the men, scooped up his back up piece and kept firing.

Each shot hit a man and dropped him, the tremor and gore spraying back onto the man behind him.

The viscera cause a second's hesitation, but that's all Brill needs. He shot through the wave of men until both pistols ran dry.

He rolled and slid across the floor to their fallen pistols as the second set of doors released more.

Brill crawled over the bodies and used them as shields. Bullets thunked into the meat, covering him with blood and matter.

One hand dropped an empty pistol and searched around for another weapon while the second hand kept firing.

His fingers closed over a sawed-off shotgun. He yanked it up and began pumping shell after shell into the mass of gangsters across from him.

Foster heard the roar of the shotgun. He yanked the receiver from his ear and ran to the building. He took the stairs three at a time.

The shotgun ran dry.

Brill swung it into the crowd. A man shot him. He spun away and kept rolling, picking up pistols and firing as he went.

He made one of the doors and ducked behind it as bullets shredded the wood. One of the guards ran up and peeked around the door.

Brill reached up and jerked him down, snapped his neck.

The last five guard spread out, weapons held ready. They crept toward the door.

Brill patted the dead man's pockets, his lap, searching for a weapon.

The guards moved closer. The lead man raised his hand to give the command to fire.

Foster ran through the door and dropped them all with five pops.

The room is full of smoke and blood, the bodies of almost fifty men splayed and twitching. Sirens echoed on the distant street.

"Shadowboxer?" Foster called out.

Brill pulled himself around the door and lurched to his feet. His left arm dangled uselessly from a shoulder wound, aggravated by the rolling around.

"No problems?" Foster asked.

Brill toed one of the bodies over, so they could see it's face.

"I got him."

Foster looked around and hooked his arm under Brill's shoulder. He led him down the hallway.

"More than nineteen," he commented.

"I improvised," said Brill.

They exited into the street and detached so they wouldn't draw any attention as they slowly walked away.

"You need a doctor," said Foster.

"It's just a flesh wound," said Brill.

33

CHAPTER THIRTY-THREE

Brill leaned heavily on Ron as they pushed through the thick jungle vegetation. They followed a game path, but the brush was worn low closer to the ground. Birds and insects screamed and hummed in the hidden shadows. They could hear the crunch of bodies crashing through the jungle behind them as soldiers pursued them in the undergrowth.

They pulled away from the noise as Ron steered them off the path and deeper into the jungle. Brill gasped as she propped him against a tree.

"We need a doctor," she said. "Can you make it?"

He nodded and froze. A young soldier, barely out of his teens with wisps of a mustache on his upper lip held a shaky AK-47 in sweat slick hands.

"Alto," he said.

Brill held out the rifle in his hand and dropped it. The soldier nodded.

"Aqui," he shouted. "Aqui!"

"The safety's on," said Brill.

The teen tilted his rifle to check the safety. Brill lashed out and jerked the gun from his hands. He slammed the butt into the teens face and knocked him down. Brill spun the rifle around, pressed the barrel against the fallen man's chest and shot a muffled round into his heart.

"Hey!" shouted Ron.

He shrugged and pointed to the other rifle.

"Let's get moving."

"He was just a kid," she said as she scooped up the rifle and followed.

"A kid that would have killed us without a thought. And he gave away our position."

"You could have just knocked him out."

"Have you ever killed anyone?" he stumbled.

She slid under his arm and kept him moving forward.

"He was so young."

"They all are," answered Brill.

They moved deeper and deeper into the jungle until Ron spied a vine covered structure hidden under a fallen tree.

"Ruins," she said. "Looks like a temple."

"We can lay low."

She led him to the black opening and stripped away the vines and growth that covered the walls. The stone was gray, moss covering the intricate weather worn hieroglyphics from hundreds of years ago.

He picked up a branch and beat the inside of the doorway. It was a perfect hiding place for snakes, spiders and any number of jungle creatures that could have made a den.

"I wish we had a flashlight," he said.

They slipped inside the temple room. It was small. The walls extended roughly twelve feet back, with a low ceiling that made him duck. Sunlight leaked through in shafts, but the floor was mostly dry.

Brill slid down the wall and collapsed.

"We can risk a small fire after dark," he said. "We just need wood."

Ron stepped back outside and gathered a few fallen branches. She returned with an armload and set it further back in the ruins.

"They're still out there," she said as she slid down the wall opposite of him. She cradled the rifle in her lap and watched him.

"We'll wait," he said.

He closed his eyes and breathed in for a four count. He held the breath for a four count and slowly pushed it out. The pattern established he did it again. In four, hold four, out four, hold four. He repeated it twenty times.

The meditative trance allowed him to assess the damage. They were hunted in the jungle, on the edge of being lost since they were so far off the trail. He was shot in the shoulder, but the wound was through and through. The biggest danger was infection. The sweat and heat were a breeding ground for all kinds of nasty bacteria that would kill him just as well as a bullet.

They needed antibiotics, and clean dressings, and water. The slow blood loss was making him light headed.

But they were alive. And armed.

He finished the meditation and opened one eye to glance at Ron. She leaned her head back against the stone and watched the temple opening. Brill closed his eyes and tried to snooze.

34

CHAPTER THIRTY-FOUR

Wallace sprawled across one of the double beds in a cheap hotel room, one hand on his stomach, and snored. It was a low annoying sound that penetrated the ear like the buzz of an insect. Foster sat on the other bed, one arm thrown across his eyes as he tried to ignore the snoring. He considered smothering the man with a pillow.

A knock on the door sent Wallace rolling across the bed. Foster sat up and pulled his gun.

"Expecting anyone?"

Wallace shook his head and pointed his pistol at the door.

Foster moved to one side of the door and reached to the doorknob. Wallace shifted left to cover him. They locked eyes and nodded. Foster mouthed three, two one and yanked the door open.

The doorway was empty. A single female hand reached around the frame and waved.

Maddie shifted through the doorway and stared at Foster.

"I thought you retired," he finally said.

He motioned her in and closed the door behind her. He walked across the room and planted his back against the wall. Foster watched her while he pulled out a handkerchief and wiped down the barrel and handle of his pistol.

Maddie sat on the bed and crossed her legs.

"We're still on schedule."

"Hands on management," she said. "I just can't stay out of it."

She pulled a pistol and handkerchief and matched the older man's movements.

"Why are you still at it?"

Foster watched her work on the gun, making sure the barrel never drifted toward him.

"Are you here to contract me?"

Wallace shifted on the bed and set his gun in his lap.

"Your knuckles are white," she nodded to Foster. He doesn't look.

"You can look," she said. "I won't shoot."

Wallace leaned forward and pressed the barrel of his pistol into her nest of hair.

"I'm not your mark."

"Lay it down," he growled.

Foster began cleaning his gun again.

"Let it go son. She could have had us both before you pulled the trigger."

Wallace let his pistol drift away, but watched her closely. One move and he would be ready.

"She's strapped on under her right arm. The gun in her hand is empty. She'd show you that one, shoot you with the other."

"One of the better tricks you taught me.

"I learned it from him."

The two of them worked in silence, each mimicking the other's movements of cleaning and wiping down their pistols.

Wallace's stomach growled, breaking the silence.

"Anyone else hungry?"

Maddie glanced at him from the corner of her eye.

"You tell him about waistlines?"

"He says he has a fast metabolism."

"It will catch up with you," she warned.

"What doesn't?" the big man shrugged. "They serve pizza around here?"

"Burrito stand, three buildings down."

"Man, I hate Mexico. I'm sick of burritos."

He stood up from the bed quickly and tucked his pistol into the waistband of his pants.

"You say she's safe?"

"I didn't say that," corrected Foster.

"So, I shouldn't leave you alone with her?"

Foster smiled over the tip of his pistol as he sighted on the wall.

"I think we can manage."

"Want one?"

"Thank you no," said Foster. "Watch your head."

Wallace patted the bulge at the small of the back and squeezed through the cheap hotel door. Maddie listened to him as he lumbered down the exterior walkway.

"He won't last long."

"He can shoot."

"How did you find him?"

"He came on a referral. I thought it was you."

"No use for his type in my company. Want to play?"

CHAPTER THIRTY-FOUR

"I'm too old to play."

She went to the window and slid the curtains aside with the barrel of her gun.

"He needs the practice."

Foster watched her back, the strong lines of her shoulders under the Armani suit, the movements like a lithe panther.

"Were you contracted for him?"

"I wouldn't tell you."

"If you hit him, I'll tag you," he warned.

She turned to him, a grin splitting her face.

"That means you want High!"

She pulled the door open, peeked out and ducked back in before exiting to ensure the way was clear. She sneaked out of the room. Foster followed on her heels, hiding his gun under his coat.

CHAPTER THIRTY-FIVE

Garbage was the decoration of choice in every corner and crack on the dust drenched alley. Wallace walked through as if he owned the place. Shoulders back, head held high and eyes on a swivel.

He stepped onto an equally dusty street in a small sleepy village. A man sat in a doorway as he strummed a guitar. Wallace nodded, and the man nodded back.

The burrito stand was a piece of plywood resting on two sawhorses, the ingredients under a couple of mesh screens and damp towels. It almost tipped over when Wallace leaned against it. He kept it from small with one hand and laughed.

"Hola, donde estas?"

He said to the small teen girl who shuffled behind the table to check on the ingredients.

"Tres," Wallace held up three fingers.

He licked his lips as she slathered beans and beef on a tortilla, sprinkled in peppers and onions. He didn't pay attention to the clucking sound behind him or notice the guitar man stop playing and move further down the street.

Maddie stood behind Wallace and glanced over her shoulder at the rooftop further down. Foster peered over the edge and watched them both. She smiled and took two steps up to the back of Wallace as he takes a huge bite out of the first burrito.

She put the tip of her finger against the back of his head and whispered.

"Bang."

Wallace jumped, dropped the plate of burritos. The vendor backed away, her eyes the size of saucers. Wallace gagged, lurched for Maddie as she stepped aside. He held both hands to his throat, choking. He lashed out in panic, punched himself in the stomach, but couldn't breathe.

Maddie studied his movements. Most people panic when they choke. The lack of air shuts down the reasoning center and goes straight into lizard brain survival mode. The brain can function three minutes or so without oxygen, so if a person remained calm while choking, they could reason out how to dislodge the obstruction and live.

Everybody panics when they choke. Wallace fell to his knees.

"Death by natural causes," she said to him. "Always looks cleaner."

Two puffs of dirt erupted by her feet, followed by the sound of two quick pops in the air.

She motioned with her finger to the roof and turned Wallace around. She grabbed him around the midsection and gripped her hands under his diaphragm. She glanced up at Foster who made a hurry up motion with his pistol.

She jerked her fists up and back once, twice. Wallace coughed out the chunk of burrito and collapsed to the ground as he tried to catch his breath.

"Scared you."

He nodded.

"Ready for a lesson? Be aware of your surroundings. Always. No exceptions."

He glared at her and struggled to his knees.

"Who sent you? You're too dumb to work for me."

"I get the job done," he said.

"So I hear. Who sent you?"

He climbed to his feet and checked the small of his back. His gun was still there.

"Doesn't matter. I'm here."

"For how long?" she asked.

"As long as I am," Foster said from behind her.

He walked past her and flanked Wallace so they both were facing her. Maddie studied them both, sizing up angles and speed. She knew Foster was studying her back, and he had more experience. More years too, yes, but that didn't necessarily mean he was slow on the draw.

"Do you want us to finish the job?" he asked.

"I'm only here to make sure the job is done. I know him."

"I know him too."

"Well enough?" she said.

The standoff lasted for a minute longer then Maddie smiled. It lit up her face and made her look like a different person.

"Still hungry?" she asked Wallace and walked away.

The men watched her go as she headed back in the direction of the hotel.

"Careful of her," warned Foster.

"You better believe it," Wallace answered.

36

CHAPTER THIRTY-SIX

The fake flames of a faux fireplace flickered in the executive lounge at the airport terminal. Wallace and Foster sat in two plush leather chairs, their backs to the floor to ceiling windows that looked out over the tarmac. They faced a wall made of glass, tinted so they could look out on the terminal walkway at the people passing by, mirrored so those same people couldn't look in.

"The best thief in the world looks just like you or I," Foster instructed Wallace as the muscular man beside him stuffed a candy bar into his mouth. Foster sipped a demitasse of espresso and waited for him to swallow before he answered.

"But we're not thieves."

"Sure, we are," Foster set the cup onto the saucer. He smiled at the attendant who fluttered by to pick it up and nodded at her offer of a second.

"We don't steal items," he said after she left. "We steal lives. Observe that gentleman."

He nodded to the row of public pay phones on the wall across the terminal. The man in question was dressed in an Armani suit, impeccably tailored. He stood at the phone banks gesturing with his hands as he shouted into the phone. They couldn't hear him, but they could see his lips moving.

"What do you think about him?"

"He's a thief?"

"You're just guessing," Foster chided. He took the proffered cup from the attendant as she returned and blew across the top of the steaming coffee.

"Study him," he instructed. What can you tell me?"

Wallace sat up in the chair and nibbled some chocolate of the tip of his thick thumb.

"He's not in a hurry. He's yelling at someone on the phone. Nice haircut, luggage must be checked because all he's got is that briefcase. I can't see his hands because he keeps moving them around-"

"No, that's good," said Foster. "Very good work. Now watch." He tipped up the cup and emptied the espresso.

On the other side of the terminal, the businessman set his briefcase on the floor beside another briefcase belonging to a second man who hunched against the pay phones, trying to ignore his more vocal companion.

As they watched, the businessman laughed into the phone, hung it up and reached down. He picked up the other briefcase beside his and walked away.

"That was pretty good," said Wallace.

"It was excellent," said Foster. He shifted up out of his seat. "Except he robbed our mark."

Wallace scrambled up and started after the robber. Foster grabbed his arm and pulled him back.

"Slowly."

He led Wallace out of the executive lounge and they excused themselves as they pushed through a passing throng of people. Foster tapped the second man on the shoulder. He was in his sixties, a permanent scowl scarred into his wrinkled visage.

"Excuse me Sir," Foster said. "Someone stole your briefcase."

The man glanced down at his feet and kicked over the businessman's briefcase.

"Damn it."

Foster tugged on his sleeve.

"We were over there and saw it happen."

"Why didn't you stop him then?"

"He went this way," Foster pulled the sleeve into the opposite direction. "Maybe we can still catch him."

He led the man down a corridor away from the direction the thief escaped. Foster tugged him into a bathroom.

"Let's check in here."

He opened the last bathroom stall. The gentle grip on his sleeve clamped down like a vice and spun him into the tile wall. The man bounced off with a small cry and pressed back against it.

Foster glanced at Wallace by the door. He nodded. Foster pulled a pistol from a shoulder holster and shot the man twice in the head. He reached in, arranged the fallen body and positioned the wound over the toilet. There was just a spray of blood against the wall.

"Lock it," he instructed and took up Wallace's position by the door.

The muscular man went into the stall, twisted the lock and vaulted over the top. No one would discover the body until it started to stink.

93

37

CHAPTER THIRTY-SEVEN

The hotel room wasn't as expensive or as opulent as she had grown accustomed to, but Maddie made due. She luxuriated under the steaming stream of scalding water in the shower, and drifted out of the bathroom in an exhale of fog. She settled on the bed next to a rucksack of her possessions, the only thing she had brought on this trip to make sure the job was done.

She rooted around and pulled out the picture of her and Brill from her office still in the frame and stared at it. She traced an elegantly manicured nail around his face.

"Brill," she sighed.

38

CHAPTER THIRTY-EIGHT

Brill stared into the fire. His shoulder ached, and he shifted trying to relieve some of the pressure. It wasn't the first time he had been shot, and if he lived through this one, it might not be the last. Hazard of the job, he thought.

He wanted antibiotics though. The jungle was not the place to have a wound, and even though the bandages were changed back at the camp, sweat dripped off his body and soaked through the gauze. Not an ideal environment.

He loved the jungle though, the heat, the mystery. He considered the bush his home, his birthing ground, and though he had operated in every environment imaginable on the planet, there were two places that called to him. The jungle and the desert.

He shifted again and nudged the sleeping form of Ron with his foot. Her eyes popped open and she sat up with bleary eyes.

"What?"

"Someone's coming," he nodded toward the cave opening and tried to stand up.

A squad of six Federales stepped into the cave, the firelight gleaming off the oily sheen of their AK-47 rifles. They wore bandannas over their faces, camouflage colors that matched the tiger stripe pattern on their surplus uniforms.

"Damn," she said.

39

CHAPTER THIRTY-NINE

Memories are funny things that come and go like the hint of the wind. Sparked by a smell, or sound or taste, the brain travels back in time to a place that no longer exists and a moment captured like a photograph. Brill sat in the back of the rocking military transport, the breeze on his face full of jungle smells and the only sound the roaring of the diesel engine as it puttered up the muddy road.

He remembered Bern.

The city in Switzerland was clean and industrial, modern lines shoving at the edges of history and pushing it back into the shadowed side streets. One of the skyscrapers had a penthouse office occupied by a small firm that financed arms deals to Africa.

One of those men stood in front of him in the elevator. He gave Brill the once over as he stepped in and dismissed him as just another salesman. Plain and simple in a gray suit, white shirt and blue tie. Easily forgettable.

"Hold the door please," she called in Swiss German.

A beautiful woman rushed across the lobby floor.

The man reached out to shove the close button, but she scampered inside, catching the automatic safety feature by waving her palm between the closing doors.

She shot him a glare as he leered.

"Glad you could make it," he shrugged.

The man was dumpy, and rotund. His suit was expensive, but wrinkled and stained, as if he wore it days on end, and he smelled of cheap cologne and bad decisions.

His head wobbled as he studied her legs, moving up to her bottom and then her chest.

The elevator dinged on the sixteenth floor and the blond stepped out.

"Asshole," she muttered.

"What can I say," he called after her. "You're gorgeous."

The doors whisked closed and the man glanced over his shoulder at Brill.

"I mean, she was gorgeous."

Brill lifted a silenced pistol from under his coat and shot him in the head twice. He reached forward, pressed all the buttons and got out on the next floor.

He walked over to the stairwell door and shoved it open. Before it closed, he could hear the screaming from one floor up as the bloody body was discovered.

40

CHAPTER FORTY

He had been in prisons before, worse places than this one, but not by much. The walls were stone, carved from the ground and stacked to form a hovel with bars, a simple square block construction that relied on gravity and cheap mortar to keep standing.

There were two rows of three cells along either side, a large jail for such a small little village. Brill surmised they must do a brisk trade in drunk tourists or jungle workers who frequented the bars and whorehouses on the weekends.

The smell was atrocious.

Urine and vomit lent credence to the drunk tank theory, and stains of indeterminate origin kept him from investigating too closely.

His shoulder ached.

There were no benches in the cell, so he and Ron sat on the least filth encrusted portion of the floor and leaned against the cold stone wall. They watched a brave rat move from one cell across the hall and under the bars into theirs. It showed no sign of fear. Brill knew they wouldn't get much sleep, if any at all. A rat that brave would have friends, and those friends would start eating what they could grab off sleeping prisoners.

He clinched his fist, partially to protect his fingers and suppressed a groan as he shifted.

"I would ask how you feel," Ron whispered. "But considering the circumstances."

"I feel like I've been shot," he grunted.

"You look it."

"This? I spent hours working on this casual cool blood-soaked look. It's all the rage in Milan."

She nodded.

"I pegged you for a fashionista," she almost grinned.

"It was the poncho, wasn't it?"

"Tourist trap couture."

One of the federales, a thin man with a mustache so thick it looked responsible for the bowing of his head that gave him the appearance of a culture, leaned around the bar and made a kissing sound at them.

"I think you have an admirer," Brill nodded.

"So long as he stays on his side of the bars," she said.

The jailer pulled a ring of keys off his belt and jangled them as he leered.

Ron scooted closer to Brill, helping to prop him up against the wall. He glared at the guard.

The federale didn't back down. After all, he had a gun and probably buddies out in the front.

But he didn't come into the cell either.

Brill chalked it up as a win.

41

CHAPTER FORTY-ONE

The waves crashed in from the Pacific in long rolling swells that climbed up to five feet and washed up onto the sand. The beach was mostly private, except for a few surfers carving the water, and several small groups scattered in small clumps.

Foster and Wallace stood on the dune and watched the people. They had driven straight through to the small beach side community where the safe house was hidden, and checked into a hotel on the edge of town.

He wasn't here, they knew, not yet. It was only a matter of time and with such a small population, he would be easy to find.

Foster snorted.

"See him?"

He nodded, and Wallace followed the start to a corpulent man wallowing in the shallows.

"How could I miss?"

"Study him," Foster advised.

"Study what? He's a small whale."

"A man in our line of work must guard against that."

"Anyone ever tell you that you're obsessed with size?"

"His reflexes are slow. His breathing is labored. He stands out where you always want to blend in and be forgettable."

"I don't think your accent is that forgettable."

"Like this?" Foster switched to a plain middle American accent.

"Or maybe this one," he shifted to a Southern drawl.

"Neat trick," Wallace raised an eyebrow.

"You need a few more tricks in your toolbox."

"I get the job done."

"It's more than a job. It's an art form. That's the difference between you and him. He was an artist."

"What happened?"

Foster sighed.

"She did."

"Who?"

"Our employer."

"She happened?"

"She distracted him. The distraction made him slow and it cost him."

"What did it cost?"

"His life," said Foster.

He turned around and stared across the street.

Maddie leaned against the wall of a building, half hidden in the shadows and waved with one hand.

42

CHAPTER FORTY-TWO

The federale was back. This time he brought a friend. The second guard was twice his size in the waist but only had mustache half as thick. There was a rule somewhere, maybe in the third world country regulation handbook that all authority figures must have a mustache. Why else would so many grow them?

Ron huddled against Brill as half Stache took the keys from the first Federale and unlocked the door.

He motioned to his companion, who lifted a rifle, chambered a round and pointed it through the bars.

Half Stache approached with a grin. He grabbed Ron and jerked her off the floor and pressed her against the wall.

Brill reached up, grabbed his wrist and twisted.

Bones popped, and the man screamed.

Brill leveraged half Stache between the rifle and Ron as he scrambled up. The Federale outside shouted and yelled, but couldn't get a clear shot.

43

CHAPTER FORTY-THREE

The front door to the jail slipped open and Johnson eased his bulk through just as the screaming started. The two guards dozing behind the desk jumped, skittered between the shouts from the hall and the new visitor at the door.

Timing was a bitch.

"Howdy partners," Johnson waved with his left hand.

One of the young guards pulled his pistol and wavered back and forth, hall, door, hall door.

Johnson reached his left hand into his pocket and pulled out a thick roll of one hundred-dollar bills.

Both guards stopped skittering, transfixed by more money than they would see in their lifetime.

Johnson held out the money roll. The second guard took a step toward him.

He pulled a silenced pistol in his right hand from behind his back and shot the guards in the head with two muted pops.

"Surprise," Johnson grinned.

He shoved the roll back into his pocket and went down the hall to investigate.

Johnson saw the backside of the Federale wiggling against the bar as the man reached the tip of the rifle barrel around, searching for a clear shot.

He never turned around as Johnson slid down the hall and eased up next to him to press the end of the pistol to his temple.

"Little pig, little pig," Johnson chuckled and pulled the trigger.

The Federale dropped like a puppet with the strings cut. The rifle clattered to the floor.

Brill slammed half stache into the bars and bounced his head off the metal. He shoved him through the open door and Johnson finished him off.

The giant man peered through the bars and grinned.

"Ready for a rematch?"

44

CHAPTER FORTY-FOUR

The truck rumbled through the jungle heading East. It was another military transport which seemed to be the second most preferred mode of transportation after the VW in this part of Mexico.

Brill and Ron sat in the back, unbound but bunched together. Two balaclava wearing commandos in all black BDU's were seated at posts on either side of the back gate, watching the dirt road slide by underneath them.

Johnson sat by the one on the right, facing Brill and smiling.

"I knew it was you as soon as his goons busted in. I tell you that was some piece of work. Beautiful," he made a gun with his finger and his thumb and clicked it twice.

"Through the window. I couldn't believe it," he continued. "You know, I was sent to stop you. I kept waiting for some gringo to come waltzing in with a violin case in hand, ready to mow down every breathing thing that got in the way. I should have known."

Johnson reached down to a duffel bag between his feet under the seat and rooted around without looking. He grinned even bigger when he found what he wanted and pulled out a half empty bottle of mescal.

"Join me?"

He unscrewed the top and tipped it back for two large swallows, then held the bottle out toward them. Ron shook her head no, but Brill grimaced as he sat up and took a swig before passing it back.

The smooth liquor burned a little going down, but the warm feeling it created in his stomach spread slowly and eased the ache in his shoulder.

"You hold it well. I never could have made a shot like that," Johnson admired.

He took another long swallow.

"I got to know something though. Did you let me win? Wait, don't answer that. I like to think I did that all on my own. I've been looking for you since DC. You did a good job there too. Did you hear they finally ruled it a suicide? An expert panel couldn't tell. Even I couldn't tell, and I knew you did it."

Brill leaned back against the cab of the truck and waited. He watched Johnson with veiled eyes.

"That's why they sent me after you. The Director and Senator were worried. Too many potential suicides, huh?"

Johnson laughed again. He clapped one of the commandos on the shoulder and almost knocked him out of the back of the truck. The man could have killed with the look, but Johnson ignored him or didn't notice.

"I wouldn't have found you but for her little group. These small-time revolutionaries like to think they're big bad warriors," he snorted. "A tiny splinter under one fingernail and they tell you where their momma lives. You were easy to find. Who shot you? No matter."

He pushed past the Commando and peered out into the jungle.

"It's not far now."

Johnson settled his bulk back onto the narrow bench and screwed the cap back on the tequila bottle before stowing it in his bag.

The transport slammed on its brakes and skidded to a stop.

Johnson and the commando's lost their balance and shifted forward, the big man's fingers scrambled for purchase on the bars of the bed walls.

Brill rolled forward and slammed his good shoulder into one of the Commandos, knocking him out of the truck. He grabbed the second one's gun, flipped it and shot the man.

Johnson recovered quickly and pawed his pistol out. He twisted to aim at Brill and found himself staring down the barrel of the rifle.

"Shit," muttered Ron.

A bullet cracked out of the jungle and split open the head of the Commando in the road as he struggled to rise.

Brill shifted so his back wasn't to the open gate.

"Rique," Ron squealed as her friends stepped out of the fringe of the jungle on one side of the road.

Johnson slid over the side of the truck and fell to his feet.

Brill shot, but missed.

Johnson took off for the thick foliage that lined the road, zigging and zagging in speed that defied his bulk. He raised the shoulder over his pistol and squeezed off four shots as he ran. They were wild but had the desired effect of making everyone duck so they couldn't shoot back.

Brill emptied the clip into the leaves where the big man

disappeared.

"Come on!" Scooter yelled and dragged Enrique up from the road where he cowered.

Brill dropped over the side of the truck and yanked the quivering driver out. He smashed his head with the rifle.

"Move," he shouted.

Ron jumped out of the truck and followed him into the cab. Brill slumped over the wheel working to catch his breath. The activity drained away the solace of the tequila and brought back the dull ache that threatened to overtake him.

Dana jumped on the runner.

"We stole a jeep."

"We have to go," said Brill. He dropped the truck in gear.

"Wait!" screamed Ron.

"He's out there and he won't miss," Brill warned.

She looked from Brill to Dana and back again.

She couldn't leave her friends and fellow fighters to be picked off by the big man.

"Get in," she yelled to Scooter as she moved over and motioned Dana in beside her.

Scooter shoved Enrique over the gate and leaps in behind him as Brill jammed the accelerator and rocketed down the pot holed jungle road as fast as the path would allow.

45

CHAPTER FORTY-FIVE

Ron reached around and opened the sliding glass window set in the back of the truck cab. She shoved her torso through the opening and hugged Scooter in one arm, Enrique with the other.

"Tell her nothing," slurred Enrique, still groggy.

"Rique," Dana chastised him. "It's still Ron."

He glared from Dana to Ron and back again, his eyes finally settling on the back of Brill's head in the cab.

"She's still with him."

"He's not one of them."

"He's not one of us," said Enrique. "Who is he with?"

"I don't know yet," said Ron as she pulled herself back into the cab. "But he's with us for now."

46

CHAPTER FORTY-SIX

Brill gripped the wheel with both hands and concentrated on the road. His eyes were bleary, but his breathing was slow and deliberate. Four count in, four count hold, four count out, four count hold. Again, and again until the pain in his shoulder subsided. The shot had bruised the side of his body and the constant abuse over the past twenty hours was making it worse. He wasn't sure if the bullet nicked bone, but the muscles tore more every time he moved his arm, which made the purple and yellow splotches under his skin grow more.

He was going to need a long break when they got free.

"Where are we going?" Ron gasped next to him.

He glanced over. She was pretty calm for a student under fire. A thought tugged at the edge of his consciousness, but a pothole dislodged it as he caught his breath.

"North," he grunted.

"You're bleeding. Again."

"I'll be fine."

Ron scooted across the seat and slammed her foot on the brakes.

Scooter slid in the back of the truck bed and banged his head against the window.

"Ow," he howled.

"Sorry Scoot, get in here." she called through the glass.

"You're bleeding," she said to Brill. "You might die and if you die while driving, I might die. I'm not ready for that."

Scooter opened the door.

"What's up boss?"

"Shift him over," she dragged Brill to the passenger door, and hopped over him to be in the middle of the seat.

"Drive," she commanded Scooter.

The truck lurched into gear and grumbled forward. Ron peeled open Brill's shirt and grimaced.

"You ripped the stitches. I know it hurts. Scooter, give me your shirt."

Scooter contorts behind the wheel and hands his sweat stained shirt to her. Ron folded it up and pressed it against the wound to staunch the bleeding.

"We have to ditch the truck," said Brill.

"Relax," said Scooter. "We're not amateurs. We've done this before."

He slammed on the brakes. The truck fought for traction on the loamy road. Ron slid forward and banged her head on the plastic dashboard.

"Damn it Scooter."

She glared at him then noticed his stare, mouth open as he took in the road in front of them.

Ron glanced up the road. A nest of guns aimed at the cab of the truck, dozens of Federales lined from tree line to tree line.

"They got us man," Scooter started hyperventilating. "We're going to prison. They got us. We have to give up."

Dana tapped on the glass. Enrique lifted to assault rifles, hidden by the back of the cab.

"Hand me a rifle," Brill said through the open glass.

He creaked the passenger door open.

"Tell them we surrender," he instructed Scooter. "Get in the floorboard."

He used his other hand to push Ron down toward the floor-board behind the protection of the big block engine.

Scooter held up both hands, so the soldiers could see through the windshield.

"We surrender," he called in Spanish. "We surrender!"

Enrique slid a rifle to Brill, hidden by the open door.

"Get down," said Brill.

He swung out of the cab, partially blocked by the door and began firing in calm, deliberate shots. Pop. Pop. Pop. Pop. Pop. Five Federales fall before the rest thing to return fire.

Ron squeezed into a small ball on the floorboard of the truck as bullets pinged and cracked off the hood and windshield.

Brill drops to the ground and rolls under the truck to the driver's side, firing between the tires as he goes. The soldier's keep dropping.

They aim at the passenger door and pepper it with bullets. The ground in front of the truck erupts in geysers of dust.

Enrique pops up over the top of the cab and opens fire. He's not as precise or as deliberate as Brill, but with an automatic, it really didn't matter. The lines of soldiers collapsed. Survivors loped for the protection of the jungle.

Brill aimed carefully from under the truck and dropped them.

The jungle grew quiet. Clouds of cordite made a gun smoke

scented fog over the road.

Brill stood up as he scanned the road ahead of them.

Enrique leaned over the truck bed and smiled.

"Amigo," he congratulated Brill.

His chest exploded, spraying red mist across the olive paint on the truck cab.

Brill dropped behind the wheel of the truck searching for the shooter.

Johnson ran from the jungle and slid behind the rear wheel on the opposite side of the truck.

Brill extracted the clip and checked. He was empty. He glanced around and spied Enrique's rifle near the rear tire on his side. He peeked around the edge of the tire, saw Johnson's shoulder and lunged for the rifle.

Johnson pounced around the back of the truck and slammed his foot on the rifle just as Brill's fingers closed around the stock. Brill looked up into the barrel of a Glock aimed at his face.

"God damn you're good," Johnson grinned. "Shelby warned us about you."

He nodded toward the carnage up the road.

"The rest of you, out of the truck."

Ron slid out of the cab and landed on shaky legs.

"Where's the other one?" Johnson kept his pistol on Brill.

"Dead," Ron sobbed.

"Bring him out."

She reached back into the truck and hauled Scooter's bullet riddled corpse from the seat of the truck. It flopped on the ground with a wet thunk.

"What about that one?" Johnson nodded to the truck bed.

Ron stood on a step and peered into the bed. Dana lay in a ball, eyes closed. Ron reached for her.

CHAPTER FORTY-SIX

"Dana?"

"No hands," Johnson warned.

Ron bowed her head. Dana didn't move.

"Her too," she whispered.

Johnson watched her for a moment and shook his head.

"Too bad."

Johnson glared at Brill. His finger tightened on the trigger.

"We could play for it," said Brill.

"Why delay the inevitable."

The fat man took a deep breath. The lines on his knuckles grew white. Brill shifted as the shot rang out. The bullet ripped into the body of the truck.

"Son of a bitch," Johnson gasped.

Brill kicked his knee, knocked him off balance. Johnson recovered, brought the pistol to bear as Brill struggled to twist the rifle around.

Bullets slammed into Johnson and knocked him flat.

Dana sat up and kept firing until the hammer on her pistol clicked dry.

Ron reached up and took the pistol from her.

"You got him honey, it's okay."

Ron pulled a magazine from her waist and reloaded the pistol. She knelt next to Brill and checked his blood covered torso.

"Good thing you kept him distracted," she winced.

The wound was open wider, blood cascading down his ribcage. Dana dropped in the dust next to Ron and took over.

"If you were a horse, I think we would have to put you down."

She checked a second wound in his leg where a bullet had carved out a chunk of meat.

"Ron, rip some bandages from Enrique's shirt," said Dana, her voice catching on his name.

115

"We need to keep moving," grunted Brill.

"You need a hospital," said Dana. She used the strips of cloth to bind the wounds and stop the bleeding. "You're going into shock. You need plasma and antibiotics."

Dana checked a couple of the Federales for a clean shirt and stripped one of the bodies. The cloth had blood on it, but it was the least stained among them. She helped Brill slip into the shirt.

"No hospital," he groaned. "I have supplies."

"Where are we going?"

"North," said Ron. "We're going North."

Her voice was hollow and sad.

"What's North?" Dana asked as she lifted Brill and put his uninjured arm over her shoulder. She helped him to one of the Federale Jeeps parked on the other side of the carnage spread across the road.

"Someplace safe," he said as she spilled him into the back seat. "Baja. Head for Baja."

Ron collected three rifles and six magazines and put them in the floorboard next to him.

"Should we bury them?" she motioned to the bodies of Enrique and Scooter.

Dana sniffed twice, and a dam broke somewhere inside of her. Tears slid down her cheeks and dropped on her dirt stained tee shirt.

"We don't have time," she sobbed.

Ron put an arm around her and drew her in close. She held her for a moment, then pushed her toward the passenger seat.

"I'll drive," she said.

She started the Jeep and pulled under the jungle canopy. Dana fished around in the back floorboard and pulled one of the rifles in her lap. She wanted to be prepared. Just in case.

CHAPTER FORTY-SEVEN

"I wondered when you got here?" Foster sipped a cup of coffee at a cafe table on the patio. He was in the gunslinger's seat, the chair with a back to the wall and a full view of the street down to the ocean. Wallace sat on one side of the table, legs stretched across a second chair as he sipped on a large glass of tea.

Maddie pulled out the chair opposite Wallace and sat with her back angled toward the wall. It still left her vulnerable to Foster, and he could tell she felt it. Her head was on a constant swivel, scanning the street and back at them.

"I've been watching," she said.

The small waitress came over and took her drink order, coffee and returned quickly with a cup to match Foster's.

"Maybe he went somewhere else?" said the man. "Does he have a place we aren't aware of?"

"He doesn't go anywhere else," she said as she took dainty sips.

Wallace slurped the bottom of the cup and set it on the table.

"He's probably dead."

Foster glanced at his protege and shook his head.

"He's not dead."

"I don't know, I winged him pretty good."

Maddie snorted.

"Wing does not work on this guy. You have to nail him dead on. Even then, you can't be sure."

Foster turned his scrutiny to her, light dawning in his crinkled eyes.

"Is that why you retired?"

Maddie shrugged and studied the bottom of her coffee cup.

48

CHAPTER FORTY-EIGHT

The flea market in the small village at the base of the Alps was crowded. Bright splashes of colorful awnings dotted the town square as thousands of people milled about from vendor to table vendor. The smell of roasting nuts and beer was in the air from stalls set up several hundred yards apart.

Brill rode a bicycle to the edge of the crowd and locked it to a bike rack before diving into the throng. He was younger, dressed like a poor student, with scruffy hair, a goatee and worn backpack over one shoulder. No one paid him a second glance.

He moved with deliberation through the crowd, searching. His eyes locked on a tall man with graying hair and Brill fell in step behind them, separated by several dozen people. It gave him time to study him.

He was lean to the point of emaciation, but wore an expensive suit. His hawkish features and narrow nose gave him the look of a predator, which Brill thought was made more poignant by a possessive hand he kept on the shoulder of a young blond girl beside him. The tall man steered her through the crowd, controlling. She looked young. Brill knew she was seventeen to the tall man's fifty-two.

He tailed them as the man steered her out of the crowd and to an old office building converted into small apartments. The man pulled her into a doorway and roughly kissed her.

Brill slipped into a second doorway across the way and further up to watch. The street was almost empty except for a rotund man waddling up the cobblestone sidewalk and a woman padding in his wake. He did a double take.

Maddie?

He ducked his head and let them pass by, then slipped out of the doorway and stalked them.

The rotund man turned into a narrow side street and Maddie followed. Brill paused at the corner and peeked around the edge.

She was leaning against the wall.

"Pardon, Monsier," she called.

The man stopped and stared at her. She wore a short dress with a low cut on the bosom, and leaned forward. It was an effective distraction. His breath came quickly as he stared.

"Help, please," she continued.

The man waddled toward her. He got within arm's reach and Maddie pulled out a pistol. She shot him in the stomach. He gasped and fell, gripping his insides that spilled out across the dirty stones. He started moaning and she kicked him in the head.

Maddie leaned down and pulled his wallet from a jacket pocket. It looked like a robbery gone bad.

She slid the wallet and pistol back into her small purse and turned.

Brill stood at the end of the alley smiling.

"Sweetheart," he said.

Maddie froze.

"You saw." It wasn't a question. Her eyes darted around the narrow street and over his shoulder. They were alone now, but in the city, they wouldn't stay undiscovered for long.

"It's not what you look like," she marched toward him, one hand in her purse.

He nodded.

"Let me show you something."

He held out his hand. She studied it for a second, then grabbed it and followed along.

Brill led her to a three-story apartment building with a front door propped open. They went up to the third floor where he used a key to unlock a room. It was empty, except for a table set up beside a dormer window. All the other windows had thick sheets draped over them, but for the one by the table. A rifle rested on the surface.

He pulled her over to the window.

Across the street they could see into another third-floor apartment.

The tall man strutted around inside, naked. The young girl is curled up in a ball on the floor.

Brill scooped up the rifle and set it to his shoulder.

"I'm not judging you," he said as he drew in breath and sighted. "I don't have the right."

He tightened his finger.

"I'm relieved actually. Because now we can share."

He squeezed off a round. The shot cracked out and the man in the apartment collapsed. Maddie peeked over his shoulder.

"You missed," she observed. "He's still alive."

"The girl's mother is his sister. This has been going on for three years. She wanted him paralyzed, not dead."

Maddie nodded as the young girl's scream sounded through the shattered glass.

"You know about me. I know about you," she said.

She grabbed his lapel and pulled him in close until their lips were lightly touching.

"What a pair we make," he sighed and leaned into a kiss.

"I'm trying to forget you," she said.

"Is it working?"

He pressed his lips into hers. She opened her mouth and kissed him back. It might have gone on forever, tiptoeing into interesting places but sirens interrupted them.

He opened his eyes to find her staring at him.

She pulled away, holding his lip between her teeth.

"Does it hurt?" she muttered.

He shook his head and smiled as well as he could.

"It will."

She bit down hard. He jerked his head back, blood spattered her cheek.

"Damn it Maddie," he grunted.

She shot him with the pistol from her purse. Two quick shots into the chest.

He fell back onto the floor of the empty apartment. Blood leaked onto the hardwood from under him.

"I loved you, you know."

The sirens stopped right under the open dormer window. Maddie glanced out, and hurried out of the apartment to find the back stairs.

Outside, she rounded the corner almost a block away and watched.

The confused policemen rushed around from the dead body in the alley, to the tall man's apartment. Another set skid to a stop and rushed into the building she had just left. She knew they would find a third body inside.

49

CHAPTER FORTY-NINE

Maddie set her empty coffee cup down and motioned to the waitress for another. They waited until she had brought a second round for each of them.

"Two slugs point blank," she said to Foster. "How did he do it?"

He shrugged and sipped with one hand. The other he kept on his waist, fingers touching his holster.

"How did he do it in Dublin? Rio? Algiers? Tokyo?"

"Is he a cat?" Wallace snorted.

"He would be through those nine by now," said Foster. "He isn't ready to die."

"He doesn't have a choice."

"Not if I have anything to do with it."

"You were very effective the first time," Maddie took a sip.

"I was as effective as you were," Wallace shifted. "I learn from my mistakes,"

"As do I," she said. "Hence, you."

124

"How did you know you had failed?" asked Foster.

She stared back at his cold calculating eyes.

"Word got around he was still operating."

"Did you hear about Hong Kong?"

She shook her head.

"It was shortly after your encounter in Lucerne. He was contracted by one syndicate to hit another."

"Mako?" she sucked in her breath.

Wallace sat up in the chair.

"I heard of him."

"His bodyguard."

"Made Bruce Lee look like a Girl Scout," sniffed Wallace. "No offense."

Maddie ignored him.

"That was him."

"I wondered what made him so angry," Foster sighed.

50

CHAPTER FIFTY

Hong Kong doesn't really have a night. The sun sets, and the sky grows dark, but the glow of a million neon lights push back the darkness and wash the cityscape in rainbow colored kaleidoscope. There are no stars in Hong Kong, unless you count the movie and pop variety.

Giant buildings scrape the sky, monuments to money and achievement. Their windows glow and sparkle at night, some as the tapestry for video commercials that blare over the roar of motors and honking horns.

A long black Mercedes pulled into a circular drive at one of the high-rise buildings. It stopped twenty feet from the glass doorways at the end of a set of marble steps. Fountains and topiary lined the walkway.

A whipcord thin muscle man stepped out of the front passenger side and scanned the grounds. He looked like a predator, eyes roaming over the concourse, to the street and back. His working name was Ching, though it was not the name he was born with. It was given to him by his employer, Mako, one of the most dangerous gang leaders in Southeast Asia.

Satisfied, he knocks on the rear window.

A tiny gnome of a man exits the back door. He's dressed in an expensive suit that hangs off his narrow frame, his wizened features hosting a scowl. Mako glanced at Ching, who nodded.

Two more bodyguards exit the car and surround the small man. They marched toward the glass doors.

Ching grabbed Mako and pulled him behind a marble column. Six maintenance workers cleaning the windows jerked Uzi's out of their buckets and sprayed the walkway.

The two bodyguards jerked and twitched as bullets stitched patterns across their bodies and chipped up pieces of the walkway.

Ching leaned around the column, cracked off two shots and dropped two assassins.

The remaining four rushed them, using cover fire to keep Ching and Mako huddled behind the pole.

Ching launched his pistol at one and jumped among them. He lashed out with hands, and feet and legs, moving almost too fast for the eye to follow. Bones crack, joints pop and men screamed.

He grabbed a dropped gun before it hit the ground and shot them with four fast clicks.

Ching grabbed Mako and rushed him into the building.

Across the street, Brill watched the entire exchange that took less than two minutes. He had provided the guns for the team of street thugs that lay dead in the walkway, had hired them for the job. The cost was cheap, labor being what it was in Southeast Asia, and it provided him with information. Now he knew just how good the bodyguard was, and if the men had succeeded, he would still get paid. The men who hired him only cared about the result of Mako being dead. They weren't concerned with making it look like something it was not.

But the street gang failed. Now the bodyguard would be on high alert. Brill played out the scenarios in his head, what he would do, how he would react. He had been hired to protect clients before, but not often enough that his mindset was in defensive mode. He was made for offense, fast and dirty. It was his training from Africa.

No distinctive sirens added their wail to the noise from the neighborhood. The gang must have the cops in pocket here, which was no surprise. Bribery was a way of life in Hong Kong.

Brill padded across the walkway past the dead bodies and through the glass doors.

Mistake. The bodyguard should have locked the front doors behind him. In his haste to get Mako to safety he had overlooked a simple line of defense.

It meant he wasn't thinking clearly. He was rattled, an added benefit of the street gang attack. Brill would bet he forgot a few other things as well.

He skipped the elevator and moved to the stairwell, jogged up the flights of stairs. It was fifty flights, so he took it slow but steady, eating up the steps with a methodical pace. The muscles in his chest ached after a while, but he ignored the pain. They had been ripped by bullets not too long ago, but he was mending well.

He paused outside of the doorway on the fiftieth floor and listened. It was quiet. He cracked open the door and peeked through. The hallway was empty.

Brill sneaked down the corridor to a set of opaque glass doors set into a mahogany wall. Angry Chinese voices yelled on the other side.

He slid to one knee and extended his pistol, aimed at the door and waited.

51

CHAPTER FIFTY-ONE

"They're here," said Foster.

Maddie started and glanced around. Foster nodded toward a battered Jeep that rumbled past them at the edge of the ocean.

Wallace shifted out of his seat.

"Let's get him."

Maddie put her cup on the table.

"Tell me the rest of the story," she said.

"We don't need the story," Wallace grumbled. He checked his pistol under the table, hidden from prying eyes.

"We need to get him while he doesn't suspect."

"He always suspects," said Foster.

"This is his safe house," Maddie argued. "He doesn't suspect."

Foster nodded to Wallace's pistol.

"You're not ready for him. Not with that."

"Try me."

"Finish the story," Maddie said.

She wasn't looking at Foster though. Her eyes were locked on Wallace. He could feel the weight of her stare and glanced up. They locked eyes for a moment, taking each other's measure. He squinted and leaned back in his seat.

52

CHAPTER FIFTY-TWO

Brill waited, pistol extended. The voices inside the room still shouted.

A hand crashed through the door pane and showered him with glass. It grabbed the gun and jerked it away. Brill rolled backwards as Ching crashed through the rest of the doorway. He kicked. Brill blocked with his forearms. Ching chopped and smashed as two men fought in close quarters.

Brill jabbed, kneed. Ching blocked them and punched back.

Mako scurried past them and rushed for the elevator. He jammed the call button again and again with a short, thick thumb.

The bodyguard and the hit man fought harder in silence, but they were evenly matched. Each punch was dodged, each kick was parried.

The elevator dinged, and the doors slid open. Four hands reached out and jerked Mako inside the elevator. He yelped.

Ching glanced over at the sound.

Brill landed a punch. It slammed into his chin and knocked Ching out. Brill scooped up his gun and ran for the elevator. He pried the doors open.

The car was one floor down and falling. Brill leaped into the elevator shaft, firing through the roof as he descended.

He landed in a crouch and jerked the access panel open.

Mako cowered in one corner of the car, clutched a bleeding shoulder as he mewled in pain and terror. One of the kidnappers was dead, the other stretched for his gun.

Brill leaned in and aimed at the wounded man.

Ching slammed into his back and they tumbled through the roof and crashed to the floor.

The kidnapper touched his pistol with the tips of his fingers and tipped it into his hand. He gripped the butt and aimed at Mako.

Brill and Ching lash out at the same time. Ching breaks his arm in half, Brill snaps his neck. The pistol fell from lifeless fingers. The two men scrambled to their feet and faced off.

"I can pay more," Mako stammered in broken English.

Brill ignores him. Ching lashes out, and they're fighting again. Punches fall, blows rain down, but each is blocked, and countered and blocked again.

Ching feints, Brill kicks and something cracks.

The bodyguard folds backwards, his shin bone jutting from his leg. Ching fumbled for the gun. Brill kicked his arm, snapped it in half. Ching collapsed in the corner opposite Mako.

"I am sorry, Master," he bowed his head.

Brill knelt and picked up the gun.

"Be quick," Mako said.

It is a sign of respect to kill the bodyguard first in their circles. Brill nodded. He aimed at Ching and pulled the trigger, then moved the barrel to Mako and shot him.

The elevator stopped on the lobby floor.

The doors opened, and a herd of policemen stood outside. They stared at the bloody carnage in the elevator car. A lone lieutenant, braver than the others stepped into the car and nudged the trapdoor up with the end of his nightstick. It's locked.

None of the officers notice the stairwell door open or see Brill as he moved across the rear of the lobby and exited the back.

53

CHAPTER FIFTY-THREE

"I don't believe it," said Wallace.

Foster shrugged.

"It's what he told me."

"It took a squad to take out that bodyguard and Mako."

"He always said he was lucky," sighed Maddie.

"He's a liar."

"We're all liars," said Foster.

"Right. So, you can't trust what he says," Wallace turned to Maddie. "Like when you shot him. He was wearing Kevlar under his shirt. Had to be."

"I would have felt it."

"Then something else. No one is that good."

"He's good. And lucky," Foster said. "It's a dangerous combination."

"He's still lying."

"He doesn't brag."

"For someone who wants him dead, you're very quick to come

to his defense."

Maddie studied him over the edge of her sunglasses.

"I don't underestimate him."

"You're scared of him."

Foster shoved back from the table making them both jump.

"It's time to close the contract," he said to Maddie. "How do you want to do this?"

CHAPTER FIFTY-FOUR

The mud splattered Jeep slid to a stop in front of a ramshackle cabin at the end of a short dirt road off the beach front strip. A narrow porch runs along the front, weathered boards painted gray by the sun and salt air. It was tiny. Two small bedrooms off a living room kitchen combo and one old bathroom.

But it was private and close to the sand.

"Are you sure this is it?" Ron called to Brill as he dozed in the back of the Jeep.

"He gave me this address," said Dana.

Ron put a hand on Brill's knee. He jumped with a start.

"It's okay, we're here," she reassured him.

He glanced around at the surroundings, taking in the cabin, the empty street behind them, and the two women in the front.

"I'll check it out," he mumbled.

Ron pressed him back into the seat.

"I'll do it," she said.

She slid out of the Jeep and kept a pistol low against her leg.

"Key under the mat?" she joked.

He nodded.

"Really?"

"Mi casa, su casa," he said. "Si."

"Great," she chuckled. "Cover me."

Dana propped an assault rifle in her lap and winked.

Ron sneaked up to the door, stepped to one side and knocked. There was no answer. She lifted the sand encrusted map and there it was, a key, just as he said. She unlocked the door and shoved it open, half expecting something or someone to jump out at them.

Nothing happened.

She moved into the house and after a moment reappeared. She shrugged at Dana.

"It's safe," she called.

Dana helped Brill out of the back of the Jeep.

"That's why it's called a safe house."

Inside, Dana settled Brill into a chair next to the rock fireplace and began searching the kitchen. He leaned back into a comfortable ratty armchair and watched. Ron set her pistol down and examined his wounds.

"Move the Jeep around back," he instructed her. "There's a lean-to carport. Under the eaves, there's a coffee can. Bring it to me."

Ron nodded and went outside. He listened as the Jeep started up and moved.

"There's nothing here," Dana announced.

"Go two blocks to the market," he said. "Get supplies."

Dana reached into the pockets of her fatigues and turned them out. Both empty. She smiled at Brill as he gave her a pained grin back. Ron came back through the door with a rusted tin coffee can.

"Give it to Dana," he instructed.

She tossed it to Dana. She pried off the lid and spilled a couple of wads of cash into her hand.

"Bring bandages," he said.

"Anything else?"

"Beer. Cold."

Ron plopped beside him and began peeling off his shirt.

"You must be feeling better if you can bitch about beer," she said.

"Give me four of them and I won't feel anything."

"I'll hurry," said Dana as she rushed out of the door.

"What can I do?" Ron asked.

"Help me move this chair," he whispered.

She struggled to move the armchair out on the back porch. It faced the ocean, the sounds of crashing waves soothing. The beach was deserted. The back porch was long and empty, covered from the sun by a section of angled tin roof. Brill settled in the chair under the shade and breathed in the salt air.

"You're low key here."

Ron studied his relaxed composure as she stood in the doorway.

"Don't worry," he said. "We're safe here."

"Does it have a shower?"

"Last door on the right."

"Do you want one?"

"Are you offering to share?"

"Just because you need the help."

"I think I'll sit here and soak up the sunset."

"Suit yourself," she said. "Nice place."

"Gnarly."

He listened as she started the shower.

Ron stepped out of the shower and wrapped a towel around her torso. She picked up her grimy shorts and filthy shirt and examined them, wrinkling her nose. She washed them in the sink and carried them out to the back porch to hang on the rail.

Brill opened one eye to examine her in the towel.

"I don't have anything else to wear."

"Back bedroom closet. Top shelf."

She watched him for a second, then moved inside. Moments later she reappeared dressed in baggy shorts and a faded tee shirt. She carried a bowl of warm water and two rags over to him.

"Sure you don't want a shower?"

He shook his head.

"I'm going to clean you up."

She knelt in front of him, wet the rag and gently dabbed the dirt and caked blood on his shoulder. He flinched.

"Sorry," she said.

"Don't worry about it."

He watched her as she wiped his chest, his stomach, his face.

"Thank you," he said.

"You're welcome."

The front door opened, and he tensed. She could feel him coil under her fingers.

"It's Dana," she said and pushed him back into the chair.

She watched Dana move into the kitchen and kept wiping his shoulder and arms. Dana walked out with two beers in one hand, swigged an open one with the other.

"Ice cold," she said as she held a bottle out to him.

It exploded. She screamed.

Brill erupted from the chair. He shoved Ron down, flipped the chair over her for protection and pushed Dana behind the thin porch rail. He rushed into the house.

Bullets tracked him as he ran, spitting through the wall in puffs of splintered wood. The windows shattered, covering the floor with broken glass.

Brill grabbed a pistol and nestled in next to the fireplace. He checked the clip. The front and back doors were open, swinging in the wind.

He dropped to the floor and crawled to a back window. He left a smear of blood across the hardwood from his shoulder and freshly shredded feet and arms.

"Ron?" he whispered.

She whimpered.

"Are you hit?"

She peeked over the edge of the window sill.

"Get down," he warned.

Her head moved toward the middle of the window frame. A feminine hand pressed a silenced .22 pistol against the side of her head. Maddie peeked around the edge and hid.

"Sweetheart."

"Madeline," said Brill.

"Darling, you look like shit."

"It hurts worse than it looks."

"Are you going to shoot me?" she teased.

"The thought has crossed my mind."

"We're coming in," said Maddie.

She used Ron as a shield and led her through the open back door. She was good. She kept her torso and legs hidden behind Ron's body and used her bunched-up tee shirt to steer.

"If we're in Mexico, do they just call this a standoff?" asked Maddie.

Brill kept the pistol aimed in her direction, but his eyes roamed toward the front door.

"You're not alone."

Maddie smiled.

The front door creaked. Brill uncoiled and launched across the room, twisted and spinning.

Maddie tracked him with her gun, fired off a shot.

Ron slammed an elbow into her captor's gut, bashed the back of her head into Maddie's nose. She jerked the pistol away and skittered after it. She scooped up the pistol and fired three rounds through the front door. There's on one in the doorway.

Brill leaned against the wall, blood leaking on the floor. Ron started to crawl across the floor to him.

"Stay," he said.

Maddie snuffled blood and spat.

"Almost like you had that planned, Darling."

Ron aimed a pistol at her.

"Do you know how many jobs I did by myself?" Maddie ignored the threat. "But not for you love. I learned that lesson."

"Shadowboxer, we have your friend."

Brill reacted to the voice like he'd been sliced with a knife. He stared at the empty doorway.

Maddie laughed.

"Dana's dead," said Ron. "They can't have her."

"He means you, idiot," Maddie giggled. "They have you in their sights."

Ron looked over at Brill. He nodded. She dropped the pistol and raised her hands.

"Want to trade," said Brill. "She walks, I stay."

CHAPTER FIFTY-FOUR

Maddie stumbled over and picked up her gun. She kicked Ron in the stomach.

"But Darling, we have you both."

Wallace leaned in the front door, Foster stepped in the back. All three pistols aimed at Brill.

"You have to be wondering to yourself. Can I hit all three? That's what I would be thinking," Wallace grinned.

"Shut up," warned Foster.

"I mean, you could get me, maybe her. But all three?"

"Quiet," Foster said again. "Do it with dignity."

Brill locked eyes with him. Foster had been his mentor once. Now his teacher was standing in front of him ready to shoot. Brill felt a pang in his stomach.

"I've seen those eyes before," Maddie laughed.

Bam.

Wallace shot Foster. He flipped his aim toward Brill only to find a gun aimed at him. His eyes grew wide as he realized he shot the wrong one first. Brill popped a hole in his forehead. Wallace flopped out of the doorway.

Maddie jumped on Brill, riding him down, her knee jammed into his injured shoulder. She punched away his gun, jammed her pistol into his forehead.

"I did love you," she clucked. "But I'm better."

A hole exploded in her chest and sprayed gore all over his head. Maddie slumped across him. He shoved the body aside and sat up.

Ron stood in the kitchen next to Foster, his pistol in her trembling hands. She stumbled toward Brill.

"I thought you said this place was safe."

"It was."

"Safe house," she said. "It's in the name."

Brill looked around at the carnage. Four bodies, if you counted Dana on the back porch. One of them half out of the open front door. There were no police local, not really, but a militia operated just outside of town. They would be coming, and they might not ask questions. Frontier justice still worked out here.

"It used to be."

"Why did he shoot him? I thought they were partners."

"CIA. Mole. Half a million for Foster, half a million for me."

"How could you know that?"

Brill nodded toward Wallace.

"I met him once. Long time ago."

She helped him up off the floor.

"We need to go," she said.

"Get our gear. Pull the bodies inside," he instructed as he limped down the hall.

"What are you going to do?"

"Shower," he indicated the gunk splattered across his chest and disappeared inside the bathroom.

Ten minutes later, the Jeep puttered down the road as two SUV's full of militia raced in the direction of the surf shack.

CHAPTER FIFTY-FIVE

The battered Jeep sat in rush hour traffic on the Interstate. A sign up ahead read San Diego. Brill sat in the passenger seat, alert, eyes scanning the snarl of cars. The bandages on his chest are fresh, but his clothes are still dirty from the run through the jungle.

Ron gripped the wheel in both hands.

"You know, you never told me your name," she said.

"Brill," he held out a hand and they shook. "Brill Winger."

Ron spied an exit up ahead and pulled on to the shoulder. She passed up the cars and took the ramp, heading toward the desert East of the city.

"Where are we going?" Brill asked.

"I know a shortcut."

They drove in silence for twenty minutes, and Ron turned left onto a dusty empty road.

"Do you know what I did in college for a little while?" she asked.

"Revolutionary archaeologist, so I'm guessing political science."

"Acting," she smiled. "I've always been fascinated by actors."

"Does that come in handy during a revolution?"

"All of the time," she said. "But revolution is not my main game."

Brill sat up in his seat and watched her.

"Archeology," he said.

She pulled the Jeep over.

"I studied out here once, in this general vicinity. Did you know there are entire villages still hidden under the sand?"

She turned to face him.

"You are the most amazing creature I've seen in action."

"Thank you," he said.

She leaned over and kissed him with a light peck.

"Shelby told me to expect it. And I'd get two million if you die in the US."

Brill shoved her back. Ron lifted a pistol and shot him twice. He tumbled backwards out of the Jeep and plopped in the sifting desert sand. He didn't move.

"I told him to get his money ready," she said. "I'm a great actress."

Ron dropped the Jeep in gear and peeled out in a spray of sand. She pulled a U-turn and raced back toward the direction of the freeway.

THE END

Milton Keynes UK
Ingram Content Group UK Ltd.
UKHW041819211123
432980UK00001BB/45